Never Use Your Dim Lights

Not Even in the Fog

D1547845

A Political Journey

Margaret Hewitt George

ISBN 0-9747191-1-0

This book is based on the author's life in politics,
although names and characteristics of many individuals
have been changed. Careful readers may notice some
persons bear a striking resemblance to individuals they
have known or read about. For instance, you may think
Helen Wright Humphreys is really Peg George.

To Glenn

For his patience, understanding and love

Acknowledgements

My thanks to Marjorie George, Heidi Pleasants George, Nancy Nase Thomas, Joan Barth, Jacquelyn Plant Gentile, Elizabeth Hendricks Miller, Karen Orbaker Navarre, Robert Montgomery Reinhart, Sandy Connard Werkheiser, and Marjory Whiffen for their help in the preparation of this book.

And to the many people who gave me the opportunity to serve in public office, I am very grateful. Special thanks to those who arranged fundraisers, kept track of my finances, prepared mailings, knocked on doors, invited people into their homes to meet me, worked at the polls, and performed the myriad tasks necessary to run a successful political campaign.

Chapter One

January 20, 1970

I invaded a men's club last night—the local school board.

My fellow members looked uncomfortable, even among themselves, as their eyes shifted to one another. In fact, the whole room reeked of tension. I noticed one of the men open his mouth, lean forward on the table as if to share a joke, close his mouth and sit back quickly, realizing times had changed.

I knew some of the board members. One goes to our church; another has a son in school with Doug; another is a Rotarian along with Howard. Everyone was polite, but I felt like an intruder.

At the end of the meeting the president made committee assignments. Mine was the vo-tech board. Not too bad, but it's a twenty-minute drive at night. I don't like driving at night, even to go to regular meetings—a five-minute drive—but I sure don't want to drive twenty-five minutes alone.

When I said I didn't drive at night, they cast sideways glances at one another. Silence pervaded the room. They must have been thinking *Here's a woman who wants to do a man's job and she can't carry her end of the deal.* I took a couple deep breaths and was about to say I guess I could drive when one of the men volunteered to take me.

I'm sure my behavior seemed strange to the men but when I was growing up, back in the thirties and forties, girls didn't drive at night alone. If we did, it was to a friend's house. Even then, I had to call home the minute I arrived so my mother would know I had made it safely. And then, on the return trip, I had to call home just before I left. It wasn't just *my* mother who insisted on this procedure, but most of my friends' mothers did the same.

March 17, 1970

Boy, did they ever gang up on me last night, and it's only my third meeting.

Since most of the members come to the meeting without having looked at the agenda, they are not prepared to discuss the issues. So they rely on the advice of Jim, the superintendent.

But I do my own research. As soon as the agenda arrives, I glance through it and if I don't understand something, I make phone calls. I have friends who are teachers, secretaries, bus drivers, cafeteria workers, and custodians. Their views of a situation often differ from Jim's. And I know a lot about the schools from listening to our children and from volunteering in reading programs.

Here's what happened last night. We had finished the business for the evening and were closing up our folders when Ken, the board president, said we had one more item of business not on the prepared agenda—a little problem we needed to discuss.

"This is for all members," he began, but I suddenly felt uncomfortable. Most of the men were looking down at their closed folders. None of them even looked at Ken when he continued, "But mostly, this is for you, Helen."

"What's the problem?" I asked, leaning forward, anxious to hear what this "little problem" was that centered on me.

"You see, Helen. Some of us don't think board members should volunteer in the schools."

"And board members shouldn't talk to teachers or other school employees about school matters," said another. "We should receive our information from the superintendent and from the superintendent *only*."

"That's right. You understand 'chain of command,' don't you, Helen?" added the member on my left. "That's a key factor in any organization. Just like in the Army."

I remained silent, looking around the table at each man as he spoke. My head was about to explode. Who did they think they were, telling me who I could and could not talk to?

"I don't need to listen to advice from you guys. I'll talk to anyone I want to and no one's stopping me. If there's no more business, I'm leaving."

"Helen, wait." called Ken. "We just think—"

I grabbed my jacket and stormed out the door.

Driving home, still steaming, the song about the nuns' problem with Maria from *The Sound of Music* filled my head. Jim and the board members can just substitute Helen for Maria because I'm *their* problem.

April 22, 1970

Today our League of Women's Voters education committee met. What a relief to be talking with these women. Because we made a study of the local schools last year, we are very much in tune with one another on educational matters. We listen to each other and we believe what each other says. Some of the men on the school board seem to think I'm fabricating situations.

When I told the women about our recent board discussion concerning the length of boys' hair and sideburns, they were horrified. A parent had met with Jim, insisting his son's right to free speech had been violated when he was told his hair must be cut. Jim told the board we should be aware of this incident and should support the principal.

Many of the board members had agreed it was necessary to be strict about these matters and someone suggested boys' grades would improve if their hair was shorter. I writhed in my chair during the discussion until, finally, I could stand no more.

"That's ridiculous," I said. "Some of the most brilliant men in history have had long hair."

"There you go again, Helen," said the president, "challenging the actions of our administrators."

Girls' skirts turned out to be another issue. One of the league members said administrators are carrying yardsticks around the halls, measuring the distance from the floor to girls' hems. If there's too much distance, the girls are sent home.

"I know," I exclaimed. "I tried to tell the other board members about the yardsticks but no one believed me. They said someone was pulling my leg. Even the superintendent acted as though I was wrong, but he waffled a little and said he would check into it.

"All I can say is, 'I'm glad I have you women to talk to every once in awhile. Otherwise I would question my sanity.'"

May 4, 1970

What a dreadful day. While I was visiting a junior high school, word arrived that National Guardsmen had shot and killed Vietnam War protesters at an Ohio college.

Since the draft has been reactivated, the impact of this war is becoming more real to many of us. Yesterday, I overheard one of my son's friends saying his older brother is planning to go to Canada to avoid the draft. His parents are livid, particularly his dad who was in WW II. Protests against the war are being staged on many college campuses and in large cities.

May 12, 1970

We are now discussing the budget—crunch time in the school calendar.

Last night I was taken to task because I think the budget is too fat. We have surpluses built in which I don't think are necessary. We don't need new uniforms for all the sport teams and we don't need new band uniforms. Besides, I don't even trust the administration's figures. So I told the guys I'm voting against the budget.

That set everything on its head.

"You can't vote against the budget," Ken, the president, said. "Our policy is to act as a unit. It's always been our policy."

"Times change," I said. "No way am I voting for this budget. It's not fair to the taxpayers."

"If you want to disagree with us in our closed sessions, that's okay, Helen. But when we hold our public meetings, it's your duty to vote with the majority," advised Ken. "We have to present a united front."

"Why?" I asked.

"Because," he sputtered, trying to think of a good answer. "Because the public would be confused if we were divided."

Most of the others nodded their heads in agreement. I sat there with that blank look my mother accused me of having when I had no intention of accepting her advice.

"I can't vote for something I don't support," I concluded.

"We'll talk about it later," said Ken. And that was the end of the budget discussion—for now.

May 25. 1970

You could have heard a pin drop last night when it came time to cast our votes for the preliminary budget. I voted "no" as did Rodney, who hadn't expressed his doubts about the budget until just last week.

Rodney's another new board member; however, he's held in higher esteem than I. He's a man, and did not oust one of the "club" members as I did. He'd been anointed, having been asked to run by his retiring predecessor. Nevertheless, he thinks on his own. As we talked together about the budget, we both decided to vote against it publicly.

When we cast our two "no" votes, our fellow board members shook their heads in disbelief. The press loved the split vote, crediting Rodney and me with bringing a "breath of fresh air" to the school board for the first time in years.

We vote on the final budget in June.

June 30, 1970

Yes, we did it. Rodney and I voted "no" on the final budget, much to the chagrin of our fellow members.

I think we're in for a breather, now that summer is here. We all need it.

July 16, 1970

I've been thinking a lot about my relationships with the other board members. I guess I am confrontational sometimes. If I'm going to work with these men for the next six years and win some of them to my side, I need to communicate better. I can't just find fault and call their statements ridiculous. Perhaps I'll talk to my psychologist friend about improving my personal interactions, but I'm afraid I'll find out something about myself I don't like.

I continue to have problems with Jim, the superintendent. He's rude to me in small ways, ignoring my suggestions during meetings and sometimes pretending I'm non-existent.

Maybe he just doesn't like a woman questioning his authority. Mother used to tell me boys don't like girls who are too smart or who beat them playing tennis, the message being that women should always make men look good. Even though I have railed against this advice all my life, I guess Mother was right.

Reminds me of a joke I read recently.

This is how it *really* happened.

In the beginning, Eve calls out to God, "Lord, I have a problem."

"What's the problem, Eve?"

"Lord, I know you've created me and have provided this beautiful garden and all of these wonderful animals, and that hilarious comedic snake, but I'm just not happy."

"And why is that, Eve?" came the reply from above.

"Lord, I am lonely. And I'm sick to death of apples."

"Well, Eve, in that case, I have a solution. I shall create a man for you."

"What's a 'man,' Lord?"

"This man will be a flawed creature, with aggressive tendencies, an enormous ego and an inability to empathize or listen to you properly. All in all, he'll give you a hard time. But, he'll be bigger, faster and more muscular than you. He'll also need your advice to think properly. He'll be really good at fighting and kicking a ball about, hunting fleet-footed ruminants, and not altogether bad in the sack."

"Sounds great," says Eve, with an ironically raised eyebrow. "What's the catch, Lord?"

"Yeah, well, you can have him on one condition."

"What's that, Lord?"

"You'll have to make him believe I made him first."

Chapter Two

August 29, 1970

I still think of myself as a housewife with few ambitions beyond the home, but my life changed three years ago when I attended a local Democratic caucus.

It was March of 1967. I was seated with a dozen other township Democrats at a round table in the library of a local elementary school. Our task was to develop a slate of candidates for the upcoming primary. Jack Rothman, a local contractor, called the meeting to order.

"Okay, folks. We might as well get started. Our job tonight is to find people willing to run for three positions—supervisor, auditor, and school director. Let's go with volunteers. Who wants to run?"

After quieting one of the men who reminded us that a Democrat never had won and never will win, candidates came forth for supervisor and school director, but no one volunteered for auditor.

I had hardly said a word all evening—just introduced myself. Suddenly I sensed an acquaintance from church, Mary Atwood, looking in my direction. To this day, I can hear her words.

"You went to college, didn't you, Helen? Why don't

you run?"

"Me? I can't run for auditor. I don't know a thing about auditing."

"You don't have to," said Jack. "All you have to do is look at the expenditures and make sure they're in keeping with the township code. Professional accountants do the actual auditing."

"Come on, Helen. You can do it. What's stopping you?" asked Mary.

What, indeed, was stopping me? I had attended the caucus because of a recent study group at church where we had studied the book *God's Colony in Man's World* by George W. Webber. It stressed the need for Christians to be a part of the political process. Here, tonight, I would have that opportunity.

"Okay, I'll run, but you're all going to have to help me," I said. They assured me they would.

And so I became the candidate for auditor, albeit with some misgivings. When I told Howard later that night, his comment was, "I suppose you know you're going to get beaten—bad."

I remained awake, visions of the meeting bouncing around my head. But soon, worry set in. Would I need money? Where would I get it? What would Howard's friends think about his wife running for political office, particularly for something about which she knows nothing? Would Doug and Barbara be embarrassed by my new venture? Junior high students aren't happy about their parents making fools of themselves.

As it turned out, money wasn't a problem. I had no expenses since one of the township Democrats volunteered to print a brochure for me. And my concerns about my abilities faded as I moved ahead, knocking on doors and trying to convince people that my lack of auditing experience was unimportant. I think some people believed me and some didn't. Howard's friends seemed oblivious to my running, and a few teachers told our children they wished me well.

I lost, of course. How *could* I win? The registration figures are three Republicans for every Democrat.

On election day, the outcome was evident early in the day. As voters came to the polls, they headed for Roland, the Republican committeeman. I couldn't hear what he said, but from their smiling faces and nodding heads, I was certain most people were walking into the voting booth prepared to pull the straight Republican lever.

Even though I lost, I enjoyed the experience. I liked door knocking and working at the polls, and it wasn't long before I became a committeewoman working for other candidates. In the process, I learned to know many voters in my district, something that would help should I decide to run again.

And I did run again—this time for school director. Working on the League of Women Voters school survey had given me a good understanding of our schools, so with a little encouragement from friends, I decided to run in 1967.

My first obstacle to running was my mother who, just the previous year, had moved to an apartment close to me following the death of my father several years earlier. Mother didn't think women should be involved in anything other than home, church women's groups, and community activities. She even objected to my serving on the church consistory.

When I was certain I would be a candidate, I phoned to tell her I would be stopping over. She was waiting for me with coffee and cake. As we sat at her dining room table chatting about our activities, I guess I was more apprehensive than I realized, because, without warning, my cup slipped from my hand spilling coffee on her tablecloth.

"That's okay, Helen. I have to wash this anyway," she said, gathering up the tablecloth into a heap and waving her hands for us to move into the living room.

In spite of all my carefully rehearsed words and my desire to adequately prepare her for my decision, I don't know what happened to me, but my mouth just opened and out came the words—

"Mother, I'm going to run for the school board."

I thought I saw her jump as though she had been stabbed.

"I know a lot about the schools, Mother, and I know I'd do a good job on the school board." And then, remembering how important she thinks it is for me to please Howard, I added, "Howard supports the idea, too."

Silence.

"It won't affect you, Mother. I'll still be here when you need me. And the children are growing up. They'll be all right."

More silence, along with the set jaw, tight lips and twitching hands.

"Mother," I almost wailed as I reached for her hands, "it'll be all right. If I win, I win. If I lose, I lose. I should say it's pretty much of a long shot, particularly since I'm a Democrat."

And then she began.

"Why under the sun would you ever want to get into politics? I never heard of such a thing, Helen. You know right well politics is for men. It's no place for a woman. I can't imagine what's gotten into you. Sometimes I can't figure you out at all. What do you think your father would say? He certainly wouldn't approve."

"Maybe he would," I retorted.

"I don't think so," she responded, accenting each word. "But, knowing you as I do, if you want to get into politics, that's what you'll do. I know that stubborn streak well enough."

She ended our conversation by gathering up our cups and heading toward the kitchen. I jumped up, offering to help but she brushed past me. I tried one final shot.

"Listen, Mother. I think I can do just as good a job as any man. I hope you can accept my running because it's very important to me. Perhaps in a little while you'll get used to the idea."

No response while she loaded the dishwasher.

"The children will be coming home from school shortly," I said, "so I'll be on my way." I went to her and put my arms around her, but she stayed with her dishwasher—behavior so unlike her.

I felt terrible the rest of the day. I even considered not running, thinking I wasn't being fair to Mother, but when Howard went over to see her in the evening, she seemed quite agreeable and told him if I wanted to run and he agreed, then she had to accept it. She even said she hoped I would win.

Although my mother was one problem, surely the huge registration deficit was the major obstacle. This meant I had to convince a large number of Republicans to vote for me, something that had not been done in my township in anyone's memory, if ever.

I seem to have a streak in me that makes me want to prove others wrong. This streak has caused me to do things I would not have otherwise done, including learning to tat. Mother told me I wouldn't be able to learn because neither she nor any of her friends could learn from our tatting friend Mrs. Brown. Immediately, I decided I would learn. It wasn't that I loved tatted lace, but if Mrs. Brown could tat, so could I. So she and I sat down together one afternoon and she taught me how to tat, right then and there. Of course, I needed a lot of practice to make edgings for handkerchiefs and pillowcases, but under Mrs. Browns' tutelage, I learned the art of that tricky slipstitch.

Once Mother was aware of my plans to run for school board, the final step was to announce it at our next Democratic caucus. I had told Jack Rothman the day before our meeting.

"Okay, folks" began Jack. "As you know, we're here to prepare a slate of candidates for the fall election. We made good strides last time around and it's just possible," he continued slowly, "this is the year we can elect Democrats." After he announced my news to the caucus, he asked for volunteers for other offices.

What a surprise to hear Joe Thomas offer to run for supervisor. He taught at the local college and was a long time resident. Quickly following Joe's announcement, Jennie Walker said she would run for tax collector. We had a full slate of enthusiastic candidates.

When I returned home after the meeting, Howard's response was a bit more positive this time around.

"That's great Joe is running," he commented. "He'll add a lot to the ticket." I thought Jennie and I added more to the ticket but I kept that thought to myself.

I began immediately to plan my campaign. My manager was Elaine, an independent-minded Republican I had met working at the polls. She and I organized a campaign committee composed of six women, Democrats and

Republicans, who met weekly to develop strategy. Together we planned coffees, found people to distribute literature in every neighborhood, and prepared several mailings. Elaine passed a basket at our coffees asking for contributions. With that money plus several $25 checks, we were able to finance the campaign.

My opponent was a traveling salesman who was away most of the week. As I went door to door, I told people I could respond to their problems quickly, as opposed to my opponent who was rarely home. To emphasize my availability, "As close as your telephone" was my campaign slogan, appearing on all my literature.

I knocked on almost every door in the district, the major exceptions being homes where dogs were within lunging distance of the door. And if I was at all suspicious that a dog lived in a house, I put my foot against the bottom of the screen door so the dog couldn't come bounding out at me.

As I went door to door I carried a voter registration street list with me, marking down the response of each voter. + was a solid vote, +? was a probable, 0 meant no way to know, -? was leaning against me and - was a solid vote for my opponent. Someone who had previously run advised me that 1/3 of the people who say they are voting for you never show up at the polls.

Door knocking can be tough. One day a man opened his door before I even knocked. I think a neighbor had called to warn him of my visit. At any rate, this was my greeting.

"Get that damn Democratic literature off my property," he shouted, "and you leave, too." He slammed the door in my face before I had a chance to open my mouth. I had planned to comment on his beautiful chrysanthemums. He's lucky I didn't pull them out by the roots.

But not all men dislike women candidates.

"Wow, a woman candidate. Right here on my doorstep." exclaimed a bearded architect, when I handed him my literature. "I never thought I would see in person an honest-to-God woman candidate. I've been waiting years to vote for a woman. You women are more honest than men. Sure I'll vote for you, even though I'm a Republican. You need money? Here's a ten. Let me know if you need more."

I tried to make a point of not ending my door knocking on a negative note. If someone was rude or made an uncomplimentary remark, I continued to other houses until I found an enthusiastic supporter. The trouble was, I started having such a good time I didn't want to stop until I hit another Democrat- or woman-hater. Then the cycle began all over again.

On election day, my poll workers, mostly women, were fantastic. They handed out my literature in two-hour shifts. One of them added six inches to the sweater she was knitting and stopped only long enough to ask approaching voters to pull lever 6B.

Part of the mailing campaign had been a hand-written card sent to voters' homes, a strategy used by Barry Goldwater in one of his successful Senate campaigns.

The card read:

Dear Mrs. (or Mr.) So and so,
Tuesday is election day. To vote for me, pull Lever 6B. Thanks.
Helen Humphreys.

Person after person came to the polls carrying these

cards. Even my eighty year old neighbor waved her card to me after she had voted. "I did it," she said as I walked with her and her daughter back to their car. "I carried this card into the polling booth and pulled Lever 6B. You're the only person I voted for because I was afraid I would make a mistake if I tried to vote for anyone else." And then, lowering her voice, she continued, "You know, I usually vote straight Republican."

Even Roland, the Republican committeeman, was impressed with the number of people who greeted me.

"Been working hard, haven't you, Helen?" he said to me during the mid-afternoon lull. "I've been hearing all kinds of reports about you. You're even stealing some of my workers. You'll probably make some inroads, but don't expect miracles," he continued, taking a moment to hand his literature to an approaching voter. "You know you can't win. The registration is hopeless for a Democrat."

"We'll see," I said, as I rushed to greet the next group of people before he tried to sway them.

Waiting for the results to come in that evening was agonizing. I thought I could win, but was it just wishful thinking? The day before the election, I had reviewed my street list and tallied up my possible votes—625, enough to win. As it turned out, the count was 565 votes for me and 353 for my opponent.

Roland was shocked beyond words when the final results were known. Not only had I won, but Joe had won for supervisor!

Elaine, my campaign manager, was so thrilled with our victory she went to the courthouse the next day to change her registration to Democrat.

Chapter Three

I hadn't realized that serving on the school board means I'm supposed to go to all home football games. What a nuisance. We get free passes—on the fifty yard line—for ourselves and our spouses. Of course, Howard loves the idea.

After the game, board members, administrators, and spouses go to a party at the superintendent's house. Parties are a big thing. At first I felt out of place, but some of the wives have gone out of their way to make me feel welcome, so I don't mind too much. Even the men are pleasant and they seem to like Howard. That helps.

But I do know one of the wives was not happy about my running for office. Just after I announced my candidacy, this was her greeting to me as we met in the cereal aisle of the grocery store.

"Do you realize what you are doing, Helen Humphreys?" she asked, pointing her finger at my chest. "Those men meet until one or two in the morning at least once a week, and sometimes more often. And the complaints they get. Anything from a phone call from a mother about the school bus leaving without her child to a father appearing at the front door asking for help with his boy who's just been suspended. It's miserable. Besides, no one appreciates you. Why would you ever want the job?"

I started to open my mouth, but she said she was already late for a doctor's appointment, and off she went.

November 12, 1970

What a horrible experience I had visiting a high school today. I wonder how many people have stepped on a pair of eyeglasses and felt that splattering crunch as the glasses crack and shatter under their feet.

That's what happened to me today.

I was observing a drama workshop conducted by a visiting theater troupe. The teacher invited me to come onto the gym floor where the students were learning how to stage a mock fight. They punched and ducked, ducked and punched, and at one point I had to move out of the way to keep from being in the action.

And then—ccrruunch.

I knew what had happened. That sound could be only one thing—broken glass. In shock, I was unable to lift my foot. Seconds, which seemed like minutes, passed.

When I regained some sense of reality, I approached a teacher standing nearby and, pointing to the shattered eyeglasses, asked if she knew whose they were.

Before she could answer the bell rang, and Bryan, the school's basketball hero, came over to claim his glasses. He was wearing jeans worn through at the knees, and his long dark hair was matted with sweat. Bryan looked at the floor in astonishment.

"My glasses. What stupid idiot broke my glasses?" he screamed. "They're brand new. My father will kill me."

You're the stupid idiot that left his glasses on the floor I wanted to reply. Instead, I said, "I did. I'm sorry. I'll talk to the principal. Maybe the school has insurance. If not, I'll take care of the expense."

The student muttered something else about stupid people as he joined his classmates leaving the gym.

January 12, 1971

I was taken to task at the board meeting again last night. This time it was about a cold weather emergency.

Doug came home from high school yesterday and asked me what a cold weather emergency was. Darned if I knew.

"That's what they announced when they sent us out into the freezing weather today," Doug explained. "We didn't know what was going on. We figured the problem couldn't have been frozen pipes or they would have just sent us home. Finally we decided they emptied the building to check lockers for drugs. Someone even saw a police car pull up. What do you think?"

"I have no idea what to think," I admitted. "How long were you out there without coats? It was cold today—twenty degrees."

"Yeah, I know. We were freezing. But here's the strange thing," Doug continued, "everyone was outside the building—guidance counselors, administrators, secretaries, custodians. Everyone. Like for a fire drill. But if they were checking lockers, the administrators would have been inside doing that, wouldn't you think?"

"I would think so," I agreed. "It's strange. I'll call the superintendent."

"A bomb scare, Helen," Jim said. "They had no choice but to empty the building." I agreed with him, but after

I hung up I still had that question as to why they had called a bomb scare a cold weather emergency. I decided to mention the incident at the board meeting last night. "Did you hear about the cold weather emergency?" I laughingly blurted out. "Can you imagine telling high school students they were being sent out into the freezing weather because of a cold weather emergency?"

"What's wrong with that?" Jim asked, pushing back his chair and sitting with his arms crossed. "What would you have called it?" he growled.

"Either a fire drill or a bomb scare, but I wouldn't have called it a cold weather emergency. That was crazy," I laughed.

"Helen, I'm getting sick and tired of your second guessing our administrators all the time," said long-time board member Jack, glaring at me across the table.

"I don't care what you're tired of, but it was silly to call a bomb scare a cold weather emergency," I said.

"That's enough. Let's move on," the president said briskly, thus ending the discussion of the district's one and only cold weather emergency.

As I think about this incident, I realize I was confrontational. I didn't need to insinuate that the administrators were fools. They just weren't prepared to handle a bomb scare.

March 30, 1971

Everything has changed.

Because of a resignation on the school board last month, Henry Albright, a retired accountant, was appointed to fill the vacancy. He is every bit as independent as Rodney and me. Probably more so. In addition, he brings his skills as an accountant.

Henry has revived my love for a good fight. Rodney and I could tell the moment he took office that we had a cohort in the battle of the budget. Already he's studying the figures and suggesting ways we can cut.

The three of us meet to plan a strategy for scuttling the budget before it's even recommended by Jim and his staff. Henry is a whiz at figures, showing us where the budget is padded and where we can make cuts. What fun we are having—slashing, slashing, slashing—as we imagine the looks on the faces of the others when they realize Henry knows as much about the budget as they do.

Henry's appearance on the school board isn't helping my attempts to be more conciliatory. As a matter of fact, I relish this new sense of intrigue as we attempt to outwit the other members.

May 11, 1971

Last night in our executive session, Henry, Rodney and I ran into trouble. The other board members know about our clandestine activities. Here's what happened.

"I believe we have some people on the board with hidden agendas," began Ken, our president. "It's becoming clear we're not all working together. I think we should go around the table and each member share his feelings about how we can work together better. I'll start."

Immediately, I raised my hand.

"Ken, you said "his" feelings. I would appreciate it if you would recognize that a woman is also on the board. You should say "his or her" feelings.

"The masculine covers both sexes. And now for the discussion at hand," he continued, dismissing my objection. "It's clear that some of you are meeting in secret and preparing budget figures the rest of us know nothing about. You're ready to support one another almost before the other speaks. That's no way to work together for the good of the school district."

"Ken's right," said Jack, sitting next to Ken. "It's important we work together. Meeting in small groups to develop strategy is detrimental to a working relationship."

A few others made similar remarks as we moved around the table. When it was Rodney's turn, he mumbled something about the importance of cooperation. I was just two seats away and had no idea what I was going to say. Henry was next.

He merely waved his hand and said, "Pass."

Beautiful! I would have never thought of that myself. Of course I passed also.

What a fun evening—after it was all over. But you know something? I'm concerned about myself. I love the intrigue and battling, but it just doesn't seem right for me, a woman and a Christian, to love being in the middle of a fight. I'm not supposed to behave this way. Maybe my dark side is coming to the fore. I guess we all have a dark side. Oh, well, I'm having fun.

But that's not what I'm supposed to be doing. I'm supposed to be more agreeable. I'll start tomorrow.

June 29, 1971

At our preliminary budget meeting last month, I learned what's really important. I had never in my life encountered such an angry group of people as the band parents—and they were angry at *me*. They sat in the front row, arms crossed, just glaring, not even talking to one another. All I remember is big husky fathers and small mothers. Their anger was focused on me because I had made some remark to the press about the band's not needing new uniforms. When the time arrived for public comment, the band parent spokesman, one of those big husky fathers, addressed the board.

"We don't know how much you people on the school board know about the band, except that it performs at half time for football games. I guess none of you have children in the band, do you?"

He paused and looked at each of us.

"Let me tell you, the band practices every afternoon during the fall, and then during the rest of the year, they prepare for concerts, competitions, and other activities. And us band parents—we work year round to provide extras for our children, things we think the board should provide. Our project for the last two years has been to raise money for new uniforms. Have you ever looked at their uniforms? Gray!

"We sell hoagies, have car washes, bingo parties and all sorts of things. The least you can do is to throw a few thousand dollars into the budget."

Wild applause greeted the conclusion of his speech.

The budget, including money for band uniforms, passed, even though our clique voted against it again. Henry says not to be discouraged. There's always next year.

September 14, 1971

Our negative votes at public meetings continue to be a thorn in the side of some members. Last night Jack told his version of the board's situation.

"The board, until recent years, has been like a noble fish [a whale?]. But it has been attacked by sharks [us?]. Blood has been drawn and once that happens, other sharks smell blood and seek out the big fish for more attacks. Finally, the big fish dies."

Rodney, Henry and I sat with expressionless faces, inwardly chuckling as we listened to this description of our activities. After the meeting, Rodney asked me what I'm wearing to the noble fish's funeral.

Earlier this year when Howard and I visited the Brandywine Museum, I could hardly contain myself as we entered the exhibit area. Jamie Wyeth's famous painting of a pig greeted us immediately. As I elbowed Howard and whispered a board member's name, the docent came over to tell us how delighted school children are when they see this painting.

Oh, yes, my vo-tech driver was sick last week so I drove back and forth to the meeting alone. Nothing bad happened to me.

Chapter Four

October 4, 1971

This afternoon, Henry called to ask if I would run for vice-president of the board.

"Henry," I said, "what makes you think I can win?"

"You only need five votes. I'm pretty sure we can round them up."

"Henry," I hollered into the phone. "Me and you, that's two. I don't even think Rodney will vote for me. He seems to be drifting away. So you tell me, where are the other three votes coming from?"

"Hold on, hold on there, Helen. Now just calm down a moment and listen."

Stay calm, hah.

"Here's the scenario. One of the other board members and I have already talked it over. He'll vote for you. That makes three. Then we have two new members coming on after the election. See, that makes five. Simple."

"It is not simple," I burst out. "How can you be sure the new members will vote for me? I don't even know them."

"Helen," he continued. "Just leave it to old Henry. Can you do that?"

"I don't know. Who's my opposition?"

"Jack. He's still thinking about his whale story. But we can take care of him, I promise. You'll have five votes."

While he was talking, I felt my throat tighten and a sick feeling come into the pit of my stomach. Five-four votes on the budget are one thing, but five-four votes about me personally are something else.

"You there, Helen?"

"Yes, yes, Henry. I'll think about it and call you back," I answered.

I'm excited and scared. If I run and win, I would probably be president next year. I'm not sure I can handle the job—conducting public meetings and facing those angry taxpayers. That could be tough. Besides, I'm not sure what the public will think of a woman president.

I know I can run a meeting, but having the press and the public present is different from my women's groups. And yes, I can face angry taxpayers because most of them are not mad at me—except the band parents. My main concern is wondering if the public will accept a woman president. I would be the first in our district.

But what about the advice I had given Barbara when she wanted to run for president of the student council? Someone had told her a girl shouldn't run for president; girls are supposed to be secretaries.

"Do you think you can do the job, Barbara?" I asked.

"I can do it as well as the guy who's doing it now. Better," she shot back.

"If you want to run and think you can do the job, then go for it," was my advice.

She ran for president of the student council and won. I shall run for vice-president of the school board. Whether or not I win is another matter.

December 7, 1971

I'm now vice-president! Thanks largely to Henry's lobbying efforts, the two new members voted for me. The vote was five-four in our closed session, but true to their belief that we should all vote with the majority in public, those members opposed to me voted in the affirmative at the public meeting, albeit with glum faces.

I still feel strange voting for myself. As kids, we thought that was wrong.

May 23, 1972

What a scene at the budget meeting last night. With the help of a retired labor leader and the local newspaper, the public rose up, but good.

Earlier in the month, bold headlines proclaimed to the community a twelve-mill increase in the proposed budget. The paper ran editorials lashing out at the tax increase and angry letters to the editor appeared daily. Even Paul, our new president, asked the administration to try to find some places to cut. He must be receiving negative comments from his poker buddies.

With so much publicity centering on the proposed tax increase, the public has found a cause, thanks to a small taxpayers group suddenly energized under the leadership of Harry, a retired labor leader. Signs on telephone polls encouraged citizens to come to the budget meetings to voice their opposition to the proposed tax increase. The people responded.

The junior high auditorium was so packed that the proceedings had to be televised in the cafeteria for the overflow audience, but even this measure did not accommodate the crowd. While people milled about outside the building, cars jammed the street, backing up onto the highway a quarter of a mile away.

Once the meeting finally began, the audience had its say. Of course, Harry led the charge for the taxpayers group, joined by local business people and other community members. The pro-tax speakers were mostly teachers and concerned parents who felt cuts in the budget would lessen the quality of education.

Finally, after two hours of listening to comments, the board passed the proposed budget containing a twelve-mill increase, but promised to consider all comments. The vote was five "yeas" and four "nays." I suspect we'll lower the amount of the tax increase in the final budget.

July 5, 1972

Our new coalition won, partially. The administration managed to cut the budget so that the tax increase has been reduced from twelve to eight mills—still too high, according to Henry. So I went along with him and voted against it, but we were the only two "no" votes. The others believed a good faith effort had been made to reduce expenditures. Maybe.

August 8, 1972

Big news on the national level. It seems that some of Nixon's cronies broke into the offices of the Democratic National Committee in the Watergate Hotel. Who knows if it's a scandal or not, but the Democrats think this could be their year to regain the presidency.

For me, the bad news is that Henry's sick. We can't lose him.

November 9, 1972

Since there's a good chance I'll be president come December, I've been studying how the current president conducts public meetings. It'll be a new experience to have my every move observed by the press, but I think I can do it.

Talking with my psychologist friend is helping me control my aggressiveness and combativeness. It appears I'm angry, probably at men. But I'm learning to trust a number of them and I'm becoming more agreeable and relaxed.

December 8, 1972

I won. The first woman president. The vote was another cliff-hanger, but Henry came through again.

The reporter covering the meeting noted that I assumed office wearing a light blue suit. Shortly after his article appeared, the paper published several letters to the editor criticizing the reporter for commenting on *my* attire but not on the *men's*. Mother thought the letters were foolish, Howard laughed, Barbara agreed with the letter writers and Doug couldn't imagine why anyone would care what I wore.

Now that I have press coverage, I have to be more careful with my comments. Two days ago, a reporter interviewed me in my new role as president. She engaged me in conversation quite easily, too easily. After she left I decided I had talked too much.

As it was, the article wasn't bad. For some reason, I must have mentioned that I might not be able to wear jeans and go barefoot in the summer now that I'm board president. I can't imagine where that comment came from.

She must have asked a question about my image because I certainly wouldn't have brought that up myself. At least, I hope not.

I did like one of the quotes: "I think of tax money not only as money, but of whom it will effect—the students, the school staff, and the taxpayers—all are involved." I know I have a jumbled way of speaking sometimes, but the thought was okay.

The reporter mentioned my visiting schools—eleven out of eighteen so far. I guess my fellow board members choked on that statistic. The paper also ran a photo of me, taken by their staff photographer. I am seated at the superintendent's desk. I'm sure Jim loved that—me, at his desk.

April 5, 1973

Life as president is going well. Nothing controversial has happened yet. I've now been to all eighteen schools.

What a good time I had today at a junior high luncheon. An eighth-grade neighbor invited me to her home economics class. She and her classmates had prepared a delicious lunch—chef's salad, buttermilk biscuits, and chocolate mousse.

Most of the students invited their mothers, but she wanted someone important, so she invited me. I hadn't realized any of the neighborhood children thought I was important.

I love visiting schools and the teachers like having me. It's fun, though I keep forgetting that school board members aren't supposed to visit schools.

Good news about Vietman. The last American ground troops left last month.

May 22, 1973

Two nights ago was my first budget meeting as president. It was not easy. Harry, the same labor leader who had stirred things up last year, was at it again. I like him, but he sure gave me a hard time last night. He sat right up front. After a few other people spoke, I recognized him. Once he took the mike, he wouldn't stop. On and on he rambled, even after I banged the gavel a couple times.

People began calling out, "Sit down, Harry." "We've heard it all before." "You've made your point. Sit down."

Those remarks encouraged him all the more.

"She let you talk, didn't she? Now it's my turn." And off he went again.

I had no idea what to do. I was frustrated beyond words and he was having the time of his life.

Finally, one of the more experienced board members came over to me and said, "Call a recess." I did, and all the board members walked out of the auditorium.

During the short recess, we regrouped and one of them gave me a watch with a minute hand, advising me to allow every speaker five minutes only. That way no one could call "foul." I did as he said and the rest of the meeting went well.

Afterwards, my labor leader friend came up to me.

"See, Helen, you learned something tonight. Always have a watch with you when you conduct a meeting."

But, of course, the main news of the evening was a five-four vote against the proposed budget. The administration will have to come up with a lower budget between now and June.

June 27, 1973

And what do you know. The administration did come up with enough cuts so that I could finally vote "yes" for a budget.

And great commentary from the local newspaper:

"Last night, the school board passed a $15.3 million budget by a vote of 9–0. This figure represents a considerable decrease from the budget proposed in May, thanks to the masterful leadership of Helen Humphreys, board president."

How about that.

September 4, 1973

We almost had a teachers' strike. What a mess that would have been. A couple of weeks ago, I came home from shopping to find Doug at the door, the evening newspaper in hand.

"Mom, you can't believe the phone calls you're getting. One right after the other. I finally took the receiver off."

I grabbed the paper from his hands.

"TEACHERS' STRIKE THREATENED" in bold headlines. That didn't mean they were striking, of course, but those headlines would sure stir up the public.

There had been talk of a strike over the summer but we were still hoping to have a settlement before school started. What an uproar a strike would cause if we had to cancel football games.

"What are people saying?"

"I think every football parent called. Several said you can't cancel games because their son's college education is at stake. But most callers think teachers are already paid more than they deserve. One guy said you should fire them all."

Fortunately, the strike was settled before school began. Each side gave a little. I guess that's what negotiations are all about, but a lot of people are still angry.

I've heard some teachers are unhappy with their negotiators, and I know a number of taxpayers are angry with the board. I've received a few ugly phone calls saying we gave away the store and we should all be booted out of office next election. I'm just glad everything is on course again.

September 6, 1973

Now, I'm angry. First the football parents, then the taxpayers, then some of the teachers and now it's my turn. I'm really burning.

Barbara came home from school today and went straight to her room—unusual for her, but in a half-hour or so, she came into the kitchen tempted by the smell of freshly baked chocolate chip cookies.

"Mom, you know Mr. Donaldson at school," she began between bites of a cookie. "Today he said you don't want teachers to make a living wage."

I was just about to put another tray of cookies into the oven when her comment stopped me. As I turned to look at her, I could feel the blood rushing to my head and pounding in my ears.

"Who'd he say that to?" I blurted out.

"Take it easy, Mom. He said it to the whole class," continued Barbara reaching for another cookie. "I didn't understand what he was talking about."

"He made this comment in front of the whole class? That's incredible. I'd love to get my hands on that guy," I said, throwing the mixing bowls and utensils into the sink.

"How about putting that last tray of cookies in the oven first, Mom," said Barbara.

"Right," I responded as I slipped the tray of unbaked cookies into the oven, "but that guy sure makes me angry. Not all the teachers were happy with the contract but the majority of them approved it. If he has a gripe, it's with his union leaders. And certainly, he's totally out of line going after you. That creep."

"What are you going to do about it?"

"I have half a notion to talk to the superintendent but he won't do anything. He probably won't believe me. Maybe I'll call the principal. He and I are friends."

"Mom, don't call the principal. You know what he'll do? He'll talk to Mr. Donaldson, who'll bug me more. Just let it go. It's no big deal."

"You might be right. I'll think about it," I said as I put my arms around her shoulder. "I hate it when you and Doug have to take abuse because of something I do. It's not right."

As I sit here writing this before going to bed, I realize Barbara is right. I'll let it be. How come our children sometimes have more wisdom than we do?

Chapter Five

September 27, 1973

Last week I went to a meeting of the Democratic committee people living in my legislative district. Recent newspaper articles have suggested my name as a possible candidate for higher office. The committee people particularly liked the headline "Mrs. Humphreys Wants to Ax Tax Increase."

"I have enough to handle right now," is my usual response when anyone asks me if I intend to run for state office. And I really mean it. Besides, I can't possibly think of driving back and forth to the state capital every week.

But some of my Democratic friends, including Elaine, are trying to convince me to run for the state Senate. Just yesterday while we were having lunch at the deli, she started.

"You're our best shot at winning that Senate seat, Helen. There's no one else on the horizon. Senator Martin can be beaten and you're the only one who can do it."

"I can't beat him and neither can anyone else. He's too popular. Besides, I'd have to run in places where I don't know a soul."

We sat in silence as I studied the check. Elaine waved to the waitress for more coffee.

"And even if I would win, I'd have to drive back and forth to Harrisburg every week in all kinds of weather. I can't imagine myself doing that. I'm not running, so forget it."

"Helen, I'm not the only one who wants you to run so you better be prepared. They'll be after you soon."

Driving home, I wondered what it would be like to run. Maybe, with enough help from Democrats, I could run a decent campaign and even win. But no, I can't possibly think of doing all that driving. I must stop thinking about it. My answer will be "no" to everyone who suggests I run.

October 8, 1973

But to stop thinking about running is easier said than done.

We're home after a few days at the Jersey shore. October on the beach can be great and we were fortunate with the weather. The sun was warm, the water pleasant, the beach emptied of college students and families with school-aged children.

Yesterday as we whiled away the afternoon on the beach, we looked the picture of relaxation—Howard sitting in a chair doing the crossword puzzle and I lying on a blanket presumably asleep. Maybe Howard was relaxed but I was not, as I lay there punishing my mind with thoughts of driving back and forth to Harrisburg—alone. Finally, I couldn't keep my thoughts to myself any longer.

"Can you stop doing the puzzle for a few minutes?" I said, raising myself up to a sitting position.

"Sure," he said as he put aside the puzzle.

"I was just thinking. If I run for the Senate and win, I would have to drive back and forth to Harrisburg. I've never driven that far alone, ever. How would I manage?"

"I was wondering the same thing," he said, sifting sand through his fingers. "But, you know, you do drive Doug to college."

"Yeah, but he's with me for half the ride. And this would be every week, sometimes at night. I would be driving the turnpike and I'd have to get gas myself and worry about something going wrong with the car. I can't imagine handling those situations."

"Don't legislators stay overnight sometimes? You have to think about that, too," he said, making a little mound of sand and patting it down.

"Maybe I should just give up the idea. I probably can't win anyway."

"Whatever you decide is okay with me, but it would be a big change—for both of us."

"I know, but I get so tired of watching men make all the decisions in the world."

Neither of us said anything for awhile, Howard sifting sand through his hands and I staring out to sea. Finally I broke the silence. "I can decide later, I guess, but for now, I'll try to drive more distances. I'll get gas in the car, too. Mother even does that."

"Where do you think you're going to drive all these distances?" Howard asked.

"I could drive home tomorrow," I said, putting my hands to my eyes to protect them from sand kicked by a little boy running by. Families with preschoolers were still enjoying the shore.

"Okay with me. Anything else you want to talk about?" he asked as he picked up the crossword again.

"No," I said, "but running for the House or Senate could be a little scary, couldn't it? Sometimes I wonder why I would do such a thing to myself."

"Hmmm," I heard. I noticed that he was back into his puzzle again and I was left alone to ponder my future. I did drive home—up the Atlantic City Freeway and across the Walt Whitman Bridge.

We arrived home to learn that Henry—my mentor, my major source of strength on the school board, my friend—had died. When I had visited him in the hospital earlier in the week, he had school board papers scattered all around the bed, showing me places where we could save money.

Over these past few years he has been such a vital part of my life—amusing me, teaching me, supporting me, always pushing me to move ahead. I'll miss him so much. Who's going to dig into the budget the way he did? I have this sick feeling that Henry was preparing me to be that person.

We'll have to appoint a replacement to the board—as if anyone could replace Henry.

November 29, 1973

I really must take a few minutes to write about national affairs. In June of last year, five men were arrested at the Watergate Hotel in Washington for burglarizing the offices of the Democratic National Committee. Now it appears this burglary has wide ramifications, not because of the incident itself but because of the attempt to cover it up. A number of those arrested are close to President Nixon, prompting the Senate to have an investigation. Already, several people have resigned or been fired from the administration.

Aside from the Watergate mess, Vice-president Agnew resigned following charges of tax evasion, bribery, and conspiracy. People were bringing him—our vice-president—money in paper bags. Imagine.

All of these shenanigans by Republicans at the highest level make Democrats believe they have a chance of capturing House and Senate seats, which is why people continue to urge me to run for the state Senate. I don't know what I'll do.

Unfortunately, Democrats are still in disarray because of Nixon's 1972 landslide victory over McGovern, winning 49 states.

January 23, 1974

Events are moving ahead in my life faster than I want them to.

First of all, I was elected for a second term as president. Fortunately, Henry's replacement went along with the rest of us. Also, one of the newly elected members voted for me, so now we're up to six-three votes. That's a more comfortable margin.

I'll probably run for the Senate. I'll have to learn how to deal with car problems, but thinking of having to stay overnight a couple nights a week makes me feel sick. Actually, I feel sick every time I think of running. Why am I doing this?

I guess it's how I've always been. It's me. From running for president of my little kids church group back in sixth grade, through college and now to the present.

Last week I visited the Democratic county chairman to talk about the Senate race. He told me he's sure I would make an excellent candidate. I asked if anyone else was running and he said he was unaware of anyone at this time. It looks like clear sailing so I'm going to run.

Howard went with me to tell Mother before the news hit the paper. When she saw us both at the door, her first reaction was concern that one of us had a serious ailment. Maybe my wanting to run for state Senate was worse than a serious illness. At any rate, her response was restrained, probably because Howard was with me.

"If that's what you want to do, I guess I can't stop you. But I think it's very foolish."

I hate to displease Mother. She had moved close to me so that our family could provide a source of comfort, help and pleasure to her in her later years. But here I was, intent on my own ambitions, which she hadn't anticipated. Neither had I.

I had one more visit to make. Since I'm a friend of Senator Martin's wife and know him casually, I decided to share my intentions with him in person before the press carried the story. As I walked into his office this afternoon, his secretary was on the phone.

"Yes, she's really running. Jerry called me from the paper to tell me it would appear on the front page tomorrow. He wants your comments.

"Uh, I'll call you back in a few minutes," she said, replacing the phone when she saw me in the doorway.

"Hi, Helen, what can we do for you?"

When I told her I was running for the senator's seat, she flicked a cigarette ash and said, "Yes, we know."

I have a feeling this is going to be nasty.

February 12, 1974

Terrible news today. Elaine called to tell me I have opposition in the Democratic primary and she thinks the county chairman is going to support my opponent. I couldn't believe my ears.

As soon as we hung up, I flew into Democratic headquarters to see the party chairman.

"How come someone else is running? I thought you said I was the only one," I shouted.

"Helen, I said I didn't know of anyone else who was running and I didn't. Ed just told me yesterday," he replied, seated at his big desk. "Sit down and let's talk about this."

"You're still going to support *me*, aren't you?" I asked, again barely able to contain myself.

"Helen, I never said I would support you."

"But you did!"

"No, no. If you had listened closely you would have heard me say you would be a good candidate, but I never said I would support you. How could I? Our endorsement meeting is still almost a month away. We may even hear from other possible candidates."

I slumped down in the chair across from him.

"You can always withdraw and run in a few years," he continued. "Like you, Ed will be a good candidate, but if you decide to remain in the race, the committee people will have to decide who the party will endorse."

"I'm not withdrawing. I'm the better candidate and I'm running," I said, as if to convince myself that I could win without the support of the county chairman.

"Suit yourself," he continued. "We'll leave it up to the committee people. And now I have some other things to do, if you don't mind."

He'll "leave it up to the committee people to decide who to support." Hah. Ed gives gobs of money to the Democratic Party so there's no way I'll get the endorsement. And I thought my biggest problem would be driving to Harrisburg.

I immediately drove to Elaine's house. We were two droopy people as we sat in her kitchen drinking coffee. Before the meeting with the chairman, we had been gearing up for the November race. Now our thoughts turned to the primary. Primary fights can be brutal. I watched Republican friends become enemies overnight during one of those fights.

Until today, I assumed I'd be endorsed, which means that committee people would work for me, and my name would appear on the Democrat's goldenrod-colored ballot handed out on election day. This is the usual procedure, but occasionally committee people choose to have an open primary in which case neither candidate is endorsed.

After reviewing the options, Elaine and I decided to encourage my supporters to vote for an open primary at the endorsement meeting next month. If that would happen, then both Ed and I would have an equal chance to garner support within the Democratic organization.

Chapter Six

March 13, 1974

The endorsement meeting last night was a disaster. These meetings used to be fun, but now that I'm a candidate it's anything but fun.

First, Ed and I each had to give a speech to several hundred committee people about our credentials and our ability to wage an aggressive campaign. Although I fumbled a bit, my supporters gave me a big hand. Ed had trouble with his speech, too, but he received enthusiastic applause from his backers. Then came the vote.

With all of Ed's money, it was obvious the leadership would support him. And if the leadership supported him, then committee people—many of whom were indebted to the party leadership for jobs, contracts and various rewards—surely would have to work for Ed, too.

Since few of my supporters owed the leadership anything, Elaine had prepared them to vote for an open primary, which would allow committee people to work for either candidate. However, here's what happened to upset our plans.

Just before the endorsement discussion, Mike, a leader who I thought was a friend, came over to me and led me to a seat in front of my friends.

"You should vote for endorsement, you know," he whispered loudly in my ear. "That way, no matter how the vote goes, you'll know where you stand."

"You can't mean that," I exclaimed. "That doesn't make any sense. We want an open primary."

"No, no, trust me. It'll be better to have an endorsement."

I still didn't think it made any sense but he had been in politics many years and he had been a key supporter in my bid for school board. I trusted him. When the vote came whether or not to endorse a candidate, I raised my hand for endorsement. My supporters were astonished and confused, but they followed my lead.

Then came the vote to endorse a specific candidate. Of course, Ed won. Mike voted for me, making a big show of loyalty to me, but he had already done his dirty work pretending that endorsement was the better choice. He knew full well that the bulk of the committee people had been instructed to vote for Ed. Some friend Mike turned out to be.

After the meeting, my friends and I stood together in the rear of the auditorium, confused and saddened.

"Why did you vote for endorsement?" asked Elaine, her brow knit in pain. "I thought we were going to vote for an open primary. What happened?"

"Yeah, how come?" one of the others asked. "We were watching you and when your hand went up to endorse, we didn't know what to do. We figured you knew something we didn't know."

"I'm sorry. I wanted an open primary, too, but Mike told me to vote for endorsement. He said it would be for the best."

"Yeah, best for that guy," growled one of them,

pointing to Ed, laughing with his friends.

A few committee people from other parts of the county came over to our group to offer sympathy and help. I thanked them, but right now I have no idea how they can help.

As I lay in bed last night, I realized what a terrible mess I am in—out on a limb with no seasoned politicians to help me, and no help from the majority of the committee people. I have a great group of supporters, but none of them has been in a campaign beyond our local township borders. Politics stinks.

You know what last night was? An exercise in pretending. We met in a firehouse where no one could find an American flag, so we saluted a pretend flag and from that moment forward, the leadership spent the entire evening pretending.

Let's pretend we're glad Helen is running. Let's pretend Helen has a chance of being endorsed. Let's pretend Mike sat next to her to give her support. Let's pretend the vote on whether or not to endorse was not a foregone conclusion. Let's pretend the evening's events had not been rigged in advance.

I'm afraid I, too, was guilty of pretending. Even if the committee people had voted for an open primary, the leadership would have directed them to work for Ed. The campaign was a lost cause from beginning to end.

March 15, 1974

Today the party chairman called.

"This could be a tough campaign, Helen. Are you sure you don't want to bow out? You'll have a chance to run another time."

"Are you kidding? Of course I won't bow out. You

know as well as I do that I'm the better candidate. Besides, I think I can win."

"Okay, your call," he continued, "but don't say I didn't warn you."

I sounded good on the phone, but I'm scared.

April 5, 1974

Boy, was I ever angry today. I had arranged to use the copier at Democratic headquarters this afternoon. When Elaine and I arrived a little before one, the secretary told us the machine was broken. No way was that machine broken.

Elaine made some phone calls and finally found a printer willing to copy my literature for the cost of paper only. We're to have the material at his shop tomorrow morning at eight. All I can do is heave a great sigh of relief.

I'm gradually managing to pull myself together. I won't pretend this campaign will be easy but I have a good committee. They met last week to prepare a brochure and plan coffees and fundraising events, but my organization is a far cry from the one I had for my school board campaign.

The senatorial district is so big I can't figure out the best way to move. I have people all over the district who want to help but I don't have a plan. I don't know what to ask them to do. A few committee people not afraid of political punishment have offered to distribute my literature and walk door-to-door with me, and some are selling tickets to my fundraisers. But the future looks dismal.

Most of the time I feel like my nerves are on the outside of my skin, totally unprotected. I wake up every night after five hours of sleep. It doesn't matter when

I go to sleep, I still wake up after five hours, my mind whirring with people to call, places to visit, and speeches to prepare. I make lists and work on speeches at all hours of the night.

Last week when Doug was home from college, he heard the typewriter at four in the morning. Since I had awakened Howard also, he was in the living room reading.

"What's with you people? Is this what you do every night?" Doug called to us, his voice still husky with sleep.

"Almost," Howard responded, nodding in my direction.

"I guess you'll be glad when this is over, Dad, won't you?" he said, and went back to bed.

This whole experience feels like an exercise in futility. Some days I wish I had taken the advice of the county chairman and bowed out.

April 23, 1974

Last night Doug and Elaine went with me to the lower part of the county where I had two speaking engagements—one to committee people in a room above a bar, the other to a labor group. Since I'm not used to being in bars, nor am I accustomed to speaking to labor groups, I guess I'm lucky I came out unscathed. Doug said I did okay and possibly picked up a few votes. Who knows?

My "Vote for Helen Humphreys" signs are beginning to appear on lawns. For some reason I'm embarrassed. Even though my name has appeared in print frequently with school board activities, this feels different. I'm scared every time Howard tells me there's an article in the paper about the campaign. Maybe I'm afraid people think I've reached too high. Maybe I know I'm going to lose, and I hate the thought of that.

Yesterday a former candidate who wanted to help, suggested a conspicuous spot for a billboard. I cringed.

"Me, on a billboard?" I said, closing my eyes and covering my head with my hands. "I can't possibly think of myself on a billboard."

"Maybe we could just put the words 'Vote for you-know-who,'" he suggested.

Putting myself forward, telling people how good I am, and praising my accomplishments are difficult for me. My mother's admonition from the 27th chapter of Proverbs has a strong grip on me: "Let another praise thee and not thine own lips." Unfortunately, this advice does not mesh well with the needs of a politician.

May 1, 1974

I feel so alone, even with the support of Howard and friends. I'm reminded of the little girl in Mary Cassatt's *Child in Straw Hat* who looks so dejected. I don't know when I've felt so alone. Except, perhaps, on the day I almost drowned.

I was floating in the Atlantic Ocean with two college friends. I love the feeling of suspension, of being held above the ocean by a giant hand as waves wash over me ever so gently. Occasionally, when a big wave forces me to jump over it or dive under, I have no trouble.

But this particular day was different. A huge wave caught me without warning, upsetting my trance-like state. I found myself sputtering and scrambling my feet to find the bottom of the ocean. But the bottom wasn't there. I moved my legs desperately searching for safety. I flogged my arms about trying to keep my head above water, as another wave forced a gush of salt water into my mouth. I could see my friends floating along unaware of my distress, and when I tried to call to them, my words were muffled in my throat. I attempted to swim toward shore, but when I stretched my legs downward again, I was still beyond my depth.

I was drowning and *no one knew.*

Suddenly, two strong hands enveloped my body, lifting my head out of the ocean. Sputtering and spewing out water, I let my body sink into my rescuer's arms. I knew I was safe as those arms gently guided me towards the shore, helping me stand when I reached the ocean's edge. The saving hands took on the voice and body of a person when I heard the words, "Are you all right now?"

Still unable to speak, I merely nodded to my rescuer, the handsome lifeguard I had admired a short time earlier.

May 8, 1974 (Day after election)

I was defeated, of course. I'm exhausted after being at the polls all day and staying up late with friends. But again, I slept only five hours, my mind whirring, this time with people I must thank, bills to be paid, and other campaign left-overs. I guess I'll return to normal one of these days.

After the polls closed, Howard and I and some of my supporters gathered at the inn across from Democratic headquarters so we could keep close tabs on election returns. The final word was that I had been beaten— decisively. We were a glum-looking group as we stared into our drinks. We had no idea how late it was until the owner of the restaurant came over to tell us he was closing. After I thanked everyone for seeing me through these difficult days, we drifted silently into the night darkness.

I know the public loves a gracious loser, but here's one ungracious loser. All my life, I have played to win and I hate losing. I can't imagine going up to my opponent and saying, "Congratulations."

This campaign was torture. What a relief to have it over and done with.

Chapter Seven

May 13, 1974

I feel terrible. I thought I would have recovered by now, but I haven't. I feel bruised and wounded. My whole body aches. Last night I had another dream in which men made fun of me and tore my clothes from my body. And then they stood back ridiculing me. And this sensation of a stab wound down the middle of my back—will it ever go away?

To top it off, I saw Senator Martin at the news agency yesterday. I tried to avoid his glance as I paid for a pack of gum, but he saw me anyway.

"You know you were set up, don't you?" he asked without any introductory remarks. "Those guys acted like your friends but you never had a chance. You know that, don't you?"

I don't remember my response. I suppose I shrugged my shoulders as I pulled out a stick of gum and departed. I had no inclination to talk with *him* about my defeat.

May 27, 1974 (Memorial Day)

I don't know when I've ever missed the big Memorial Day

parade in town, but I sure didn't feel like seeing people this morning. I roamed around the house awhile and then decided to attack my long-neglected garden.

With every clump of weeds I yanked from the ground, I felt I was yanking the rotten filthy politicians out of my life. Before the morning was over, I had accumulated a huge pile of weeds. I felt like burning them to imagine the politicians disappearing into nothingness, but Howard reminded me of the anti-leaf burning ordinance, so we piled the debris onto an old sheet and he hauled everything into the woods behind the house. It will be good mulch for our May apples, Jack-in-the-pulpits, and young dogwoods.

Now maybe I can continue with life. But, one thing is for sure, I am finished with politics for all time. I can't believe I once thought it was fun.

Next week, I have to give a speech to a women's history class at the local college. I wonder what I'll say, now that I'm no longer a politician.

June 4, 1974

Today my life in politics is over for good. It ended with my speech at the community college. Until this morning I had no idea what I was going to say. What do losers say to college students?

Should I tell them I was a wounded person, sick at heart over the deceptions inflicted upon me by friends? Should I reveal that would-be supporters were bought off by promises of jobs or lucrative contracts? Should I tell them that some people were actually threatened with the loss of their jobs? Should I tell them how a small group of people controls election outcomes through the use of money, favors and patronage?

Or, since it's college students, must I nurture the myth that politics can be a virtuous calling and that by being involved in politics, a person can have a positive impact on the lives of others? I really didn't know which path I would take.

However, just as I awoke this morning, my mind jumped to the day long ago when my mother warned me about playing with the big boys. I decided to tell the story to the students.

I was eight, sitting on the front steps of our house near the top of a hill, watching my older brother and his friends play kick-the-can.

When I played kick-the-can with my friends, I was the fastest one at retrieving the can and tagging others out. So when one of the boys was called home for lunch, I was quick to respond when my brother yelled, "Hey, Helen, you wanna play?"

"Sure," I said as I raced to join them.

One of the other boys moaned, "She's too little, and besides she's a girl."

"Oh, let Little Miss Muffet play," sneered Bob, one of the bigger boys. "Maybe we can have some fun."

Right away I was It. Bob kicked the can down the hill. This was against the rules when I played with my friends, but I tore after it and dashed back home, which was a manhole cover in the center of the intersection. I had barely put the can down when another boy rushed past me almost knocking me over as he kicked the can even farther down the hill. I heard the boys laugh as I sped after it.

Out of breath, my legs aching, I rushed back up the hill a second time. Just as I put the can down, Bob sneaked up behind me and kicked the can down the hill again.

"Having fun, are you, Helen?" Bob asked as he gave me a little shove, pushing me off balance.

I knew I was defeated. Tears streaming down my face, I stumbled home to my mother who was preparing lunch. When I told her the boys didn't play fair and they laughed at me, she enfolded me in the warmth of her arms. But her scolding response was one that I remember to this day.

"Helen, you should know better than to play with the big boys."

A hush fell over the classroom as I ended my story. A few heads nodded in acknowledgement of a shared experience. Others sat immobile staring into space as if they, too, were pulling up a similar awakening from their childhood memories.

Suddenly, we were jolted from our quietness by one of the few male students who blurted out, "Do you expect us to believe this kid story has something to do with your getting defeated?"

"Be quiet, John," shot out a young woman sitting in the back.

"John has every right to his opinion," called out another woman. "I don't think this story has anything to do with politics either."

"Yes, it does," I answered. "From the moment I announced my intention to run, the big boys let me play.

"They rigged the endorsement meeting which eliminated my chance of receiving party campaign funds. They watched with glee as I ran myself ragged knocking on doors, as I foraged for money to finance my advertising costs, and as I attempted to crash the news media they controlled. While I snagged a vote here, a vote there, they watched in enjoyment, knowing my efforts were in vain. I might as well have run home to my mother."

No one spoke—not the students, not the professor, not I.

Finally, one of the students pointed to the clock on the wall and I realized the hour was up. I nodded my head to the students as they, without saying a word, gathered up their belongings and filed out of the room.

Driving home I felt a sense of relief spread throughout my body and I felt at peace. Never again will I have to talk to anyone about politics.

Chapter Eight

July 16, 1974

Late last month I had a new school board experience—redistricting. If I had thought band uniforms and tax increases brought out the emotions, I had another good lesson. So many parents showed up at our meeting, we had to move from our boardroom to the school auditorium next door.

Since one of our elementary schools is bulging at the seams, it's necessary to move some of these children to other schools. The administration drew up a plan which appeared okay to the board, but darned if some parents didn't come up with a better plan that would cause less upheaval in the community.

Board members like to support the administration on most issues but since the parents' plan seemed better, we asked the administration to reconsider all options.

The parents left the meeting happy. We had listened to them.

August 10, 1974

Yesterday Nixon resigned as a result of the Watergate

break-in and cover-up. Our new president is Gerald Ford, handpicked by Nixon following the resignation of Agnew.

Voice-activated electronic tapes, installed in the Oval Office in 1971 by President Nixon, became his downfall. The tapes clearly revealed his complicity in the cover-up of the Watergate burglary of the Democratic National Committee in June of 1972.

Last month the House committee approved three articles of impeachment and Nixon resigned yesterday.

Democrats across the nation are jubilant, seeing an opportunity to win back the presidency in 1976. As for me, I feel unwelcome stirrings within me. I can't imagine that I am thinking of running again, but wouldn't it be great to be a part of a big Democratic sweep?

December 2, 1974

I've had fun visiting schools these past few months. Many teachers are happy to have board members see the innovative practices they use in their classrooms.

One teacher has a club on orienteering. I had never heard the term before. The children learn how to read maps, use the compass and figure out directions with a minimum of landmarks. I joined them on the playground as we zigzagged all over the area with maps and compasses.

Yesterday I visited a class where the children were making music even though many of them had no musical talent. They were playing Orff instruments, using five notes—C, D, E, G, and A. Supposedly these notes sound good together—and they do. Percussion instruments rounded out the band.

I'm having a good time. Even the weather has been

pleasant for the football games. And I feel so free now that I'm finishing my term as president and don't have any more elections to worry about. Of course, Elaine still keeps dragging me to Democratic committee meetings.

Oh yes, Ed, my opponent in the primary, was defeated by Senator Martin last month. I would have been, too.

May 20, 1975

Budget time again. Aside from our usual audience of teachers, parents, and taxpayers, this year the local Chamber of Commerce has found a cause—no tax increase. Thank goodness, I'm no longer president.

Before the meeting last night I was chatting with one of the members of the Chamber of Commerce. When I mentioned I was sorry the budget had become such a divisive issue, I wasn't expecting a Shakespearean response.

"'All the world's a stage, And all the men and women merely players,'" he said, rolling the quote off his tongue, his eyes dancing. "Don't you understand, Helen? This is just one great big drama here tonight with all of us acting our parts. You're the advocate for the school board's position for modest tax increases, my role is to support the position of the Chamber of Commerce for no tax increase, and the teachers are the chorus in the background calling for higher taxes. We're all just actors. So, come on, Helen. Enjoy the play."

I guess it's true that much of what we do is acting. Many days I look in the mirror and think *You phony. Look at yourself. Think you're Mrs. Hot Shot, running all over the place as president of the school board, candidate for state office, but you're just a housewife, pretending you're something else.*

Most of the time I can move into my role well, but I was never comfortable with the role of candidate for the Senate. If I had thought I could win, I suppose I would have felt better about myself.

Chapter Nine

June 24, 1975

We lowered the rate of the tax increase slightly, and the budget passed 9-0. But that's not my big news.

Last night at the Democratic club meeting, much of the talk was about the difficulties for the Republican party —Agnew, Nixon, and this new word in our political vocabulary, Watergate. We all agreed that 1976 would be a good year for Democratic candidates.

"As a matter of fact, Helen," said the club president, "we want you to run for state representative."

"Me! You can't be serious. After what I went through. What's with you people? No way will I go through that again. I'm not a masochist, you know. Let someone else have all the fun," I concluded with a grunt.

"Just think about it—please. We can talk later," said Elaine, as she nodded to the president that the subject was closed for the moment.

You guessed it. I didn't sleep much last night. For all my protesting, politics is in my blood.

The state Assembly district is a smaller area than the Senate district and I know many more people than before. I'm sure I can find workers—both Republicans and Democrats. I even imagined I could win. But then common sense prevailed. I am finished with being a candidate—and worries about driving to Harrisburg.

September 10, 1975

Today Elaine and I visited our friend Ruth, also a committeewoman. While enjoying the last swim of the season, politics was the main topic of conversation.

The presidential race is shaping up. Ford looks like a shoo-in for the Republican nomination and now it appears the governor of Georgia, Jimmy Carter, may make a stab at the presidency. Even my dentist is talking about Carter. The other day, with both his hands in my mouth, he mused about the idea of having a president named "Jimmy" and found it undignified.

As we were drying ourselves after our swim and were just about to have some iced tea, Elaine said, "Helen, you've got to run again. There's no other Democrat who has the experience you have. And besides, lots of people want you to run."

"Elaine's right, Helen," joined in Ruth. " We're hoping you'll announce your candidacy for the House at the next meeting. We know everyone will think it's a great idea."

"Listen, both of you," I responded, taking off my dark glasses so they could both see the look in my eyes, "it takes a lot more than twenty people sitting in a room to win an election. The answer is no. Don't you dare mention my name and besides I can't unseat Bob. He's been in the House forever."

I threw down my towel and dove back into the pool.

I'm annoyed that people are trying to make me run. Don't they understand what it was like last time? Aside from all the unpleasantness, I don't even know if I have the stamina to gear up for another campaign. I feel like pulling a blanket over my head and disappearing.

November 11, 1975

I hate to put this in writing but I'm beginning to get the urge to run for office again. I am tempted because Bob, the incumbent House member, has now decided to run for the congressional seat, which is being vacated. Therefore, Bob's seat in the Pennsylvania House will be open—no incumbent for me to defeat. Still, with the Democrats out-registered 20,500 to 9,700, I'm nuts to even think about running.

Oh, yes, we now have two more women on the school board—one elected in '73 and one elected earlier this month.

January 19, 1976

This may be the year the Democrats can win back the White House and the year I'll run for the Legislature. If I run, I sure want to win.

An open seat and scandals within the opposition party is the dream of every candidate. A real chance to win.

Louis Pasteur said "...chance favors only the prepared mind."

I think my mind is almost prepared. During the Christmas holidays I studied former voting patterns in the legislative district. I know I'll have strong support from voters in this school district; and several municipalities have elected Democrats to their councils. But strong Republican areas could be a problem. My chance of winning will depend on independent voters and crossover Republicans.

I talked it over with Howard the other evening. As usual, he said if that's what I wanted to do, he'd support my decision.

January 21, 1976

Today Elaine and I stopped to see the county chairman.

"What are you two up to?" he asked in a friendly manner. He and I had patched things up after my disastrous Senate race.

"Helen's going to run for the House," blurted out Elaine.

"Sounds good to me," he responded. "As opposed to your last race, Helen, I'm almost certain no one else is interested. Go for it."

"Will you support me?" I asked, still not hearing those magic words.

"I expect to, unless something very unexpected happens."

At least I think I know where I stand. I'm off and running.

February 3, 1976

Yesterday Howard went with me to break the news to Mother.

When she saw us arrive together during the daytime, she suspected illness again.

"What's wrong?" she asked, even before she kissed us. "Are you both all right? Neither of you has to have surgery, do you?"

"No, Mother, we're both okay, but we have something

to tell you," responded Howard, as we moved into her living room.

"Don't tell me," she said, putting her hands to her chest. "Helen, you're not going back into politics again, are you? I hope it's nothing that crazy."

Here it was. There was nothing to do but tell her.

"It's not crazy, Mother, and yes, I'm going to make another try at it. But this time, I'm going to run for the House of Representatives." I started out slowly but found myself hurrying through the rest of my announcement. "It's not as big an area as the senatorial district, I won't be running against an incumbent, and I have a good chance of winning."

"Howard," she said, looking at him beseechingly. "Can't you do anything with her?" Before he could answer, she continued with me. "Why do you do this, Helen? You know how unpleasant it was when you ran before. And those awful pictures of you they printed in the newspapers. How can you stand going through that again?"

"It'll be different this time, Mother. I learned so much from the last race and it won't be the same. It's a smaller area and I already know a lot of people. I really think I can win."

"If you win, then you'll have to go to Harrisburg and then how will your family make out? Howard, you don't want her going off to Harrisburg, do you?" she pleaded.

"If that's what she wants to do, it's okay with me. We'll make out. The children are older now. Goodness, Doug's in college and Barbara will be going next year," he assured her.

We stayed awhile talking about the children and some of our other activities, but we could tell her mind was far away. She didn't respond to anything we said.

I feel awful. I hope she comes around to being supportive.

Chapter Ten

March 10, 1976

Enthusiasm ran high last night as committee people discussed the possibility of electing Democrats this year, maybe even a Democratic president.

People volunteered to help me with coffees, mailings, and even walking door-to-door with me in their communities. I'm anxious to begin.

Since I don't have any primary opposition, I have plenty of time for organizing, but I'm worried about a large township in the southern part of the district where I don't know a single Republican. It's a big area and I need Republican votes, lots of them. I've met some of the Democrats from there at various committee meetings, but the Republicans outnumber the Democrats by a huge majority.

I said I didn't know a single Republican. I take it back. I do know one Republican—Joan Harris. We met while serving on the county heart fund drive last year. Maybe I'll call her.

March 25, 1976

I had a stroke of luck this morning. In between door knocking and visiting Mother, I darted into the bookstore to buy a birthday card for my brother. As I entered, the owner called out, "How's the campaign going, Helen?"

A woman who was just about to walk out the door turned, tilted her head and said, "You're not Helen Humphreys, are you?"

"Yes," I responded. "Who are you?"

"Harriet Fox. I'm a new Democratic committeewoman in that huge Republican township, and I've been dying to meet you. I do so want to work for you."

"It's great to meet you, Harriet. And I need all the help I can get. One of the first things I need to do is meet more of you Democrats. Any ideas how I can do that?"

"We were just talking about inviting you to our next township Democratic club meeting. Would you come? I must tell you, everyone is so excited about your running. We all want to help."

"Sounds good. When's the next meeting?" I asked as I reached for my pocket calendar.

"Third Tuesday. Can you come?"

"Yep. I'll mark my calendar right now. All I need are the details—time and place."

And from that chance encounter came many more workers and friends.

April 6, 1976

Joan Harris, the heart fund person, is now on board to help. A mutual friend brought us together for lunch today. I couldn't believe my good fortune when I heard her response.

"Sure, I'd love to help you. How about if I begin by inviting a group of friends to a coffee in my home? They'll have a chance to meet you and I'm sure many of them will help, any way they can. What do you need?

"Everything—help with mailings, poll workers, coffees, all kinds of things."

"I think we can get workers for you. Should be fun," said Joan with a big smile on her face. "But I'm sure you already know, Democrats never win in our township. We have a huge Republican majority, but I guess you know that."

"Yes, I know, but if we can encourage a large number of Republicans to vote for me, I may be able to garner enough votes other places to cut my losses. But I know my winning is a long shot." We all laughed at the incongruity of our sitting over a pleasant lunch, thinking we could change election practices that had been in existence for as long as anyone could remember.

"We'll give it a try," Joan said as she mentioned names of people she would invite to meet me. We decided to wait until summer to attempt any kind of a get-together. Then we'll have a better idea of the kind of help we'll need.

May 5, 1976 (Day after primary election)

Even though I'm running unopposed, it's important for me to meet as many people as I can. So I worked the polls all day yesterday, spending a half-hour at one polling place and then driving off to another. I was all over the district, even where Joan and Harriet live. I met a lot of pleasant people, both Democrats and Republicans, but I received a fair amount of razzing from the Republican committee people who told me I'm nuts to even think I can win. They treat me like a friendly ghost balloon—something to poke out every once in a while but certainly no one to be afraid of.

I surprised voters by greeting them as they left the polls and handing them my flyer. At first they thought I didn't understand that they had already voted, but they soon caught on when I introduced myself and asked for their support in the fall. Many, but certainly not all, gave me an encouraging smile.

Today was fun but now the hard work begins.

Oh yes, the Republicans chose another salesman to run against me, the same as when I won my school board election.

June 18, 1976

The "Elect Helen Humphreys Campaign Committee," a mixture of Republicans and Democrats and men and women, is off to a good start. Our mailing chairperson is having an all-day party at her house for people to prepare 10,000 letters for our major mailing. The flyer, complete with family photo, is at the printer's. We'll also need bumper stickers and posters for lawn signs. Dates are confirmed for a champagne brunch and several luncheons. So far, nine coffees have been lined up. For fundraising, I'll send out a letter to selected people, hoping to receive substantial money. And of course we'll ask for money at coffees, wine and cheese parties, and any other way we can think of.

The committee chair, a Republican, is very organized, making sure members follow through with their tasks. Elaine will work mostly with Democratic committee people.

I'm beginning to feel I am not alone.

July 18, 1976

Yesterday was the big county fair. The huge grassy field was a mass of parked cars, tents, and people milling about.

Overarching all was the aroma of barbecued chicken cooking over open grills. I was to meet Elaine and other volunteers at the gate.

Since I was early and the others hadn't arrived, I wandered around the fairgrounds, carrying my brochures in a tote bag slung over my shoulder. I knew I was supposed to talk to people. That's what politicians do. But I seemed to have a terrible problem—stage fright. I felt disorientated, lonely, and totally unable to function. I wanted to go up to people and hand out my brochures, but instead, I felt like hiding. If I hadn't expected the others to come any moment, I think I would have returned home.

But then I spotted my friend Jack, or rather he spotted me. He'd been a candidate in many elections and had helped me in my Senate campaign.

"What kind of a reception are you getting?" he asked right off the bat.

"I don't know. I haven't talked to anyone yet," I laughed as though a politician's not talking to anyone was perfectly normal.

"How come? Did you just get here?"

"No, I've been here a little while, but I can't figure out where to begin," I said, throwing my hands in the air and looking around at the mob of people.

"What do you mean, you don't know where to begin?" he scorned. "I'll never forget the hit you made at the mall, handing out your Senate literature until the guards chased you." He paused. "You do know that was another one of those dirty tricks played on you, don't you?"

"I don't understand," I said.

"You were having too much success, so our friend Jimmy sicked the guards on you. There wasn't any reason you couldn't hand out literature at the mall. Plenty of candidates do."

I wanted to ask Jack more about that incident, but he kept on talking.

"Just go up to someone and say, `Hi, I'm Helen Humphreys. I'm running for the Legislature.' What are they going to do to you? The worst they can do is tell you they're voting for your opponent."

"I know, I know," I sighed. "I just can't get started."

"Look over there," pointed Jack. "See that line for the chicken barbecue? Those people have a half-hour to kill. They have nothing to do but stand and look around. They might as well be reading your brochure as anything else.

"Go on. I've got to find my family. Maybe I'll catch up with you later and you can tell me about the wonderful contacts you've made."

Slowly I made my way to the barbecue line. A young woman dressed in a hot pink jogging suit appeared to be alone, so I began with her.

"Hi, my name's Helen Humphreys. I'm running—"

"Helen Humphreys," she exclaimed. "I've been dying to meet you. I think it's great you're running. I've read so many wonderful things about you."

"Thanks. You don't know how good those words sound. What's your name?" I asked as I reached in my pocket for my pen and notebook.

"Marilyn. Marilyn Landwehr."

She was a lawyer with a prestigious firm in a town where I knew very few people. When she said she would do anything to help me get elected, I could hardly believe my good fortune.

As Marilyn and I talked together in the barbecue line, other people were drawn into our conversation and held out their hands for my literature. Some even offered to help and one woman whipped out her checkbook.

The rest of the day was easy compared to that mall

experience Jack mentioned. It was a Sunday afternoon during my Senate campaign when several of us Democratic candidates, all running against the endorsed slate, met at the mall to campaign. Even the gubernatorial candidate, a popular activist, was there. He was the one attracting attention, but all of us handed out our literature. We were near the escalators when suddenly, several men accompanied by a security guard approached us.

"No politicians allowed," said the guard.

"Since when?" asked one of the candidates. "Politicians are here all the time."

"Leave. I said it's against the rules."

Most of the candidates left, but two of us went to another section of the mall, thinking the candidate for governor was the target of attention. It wasn't long before the security guard found us.

"You've been warned. Leave. Now," he shouted.

We left.

July 28, 1976

Joan's coffee today produced wonderful results. Some of the women had already met me at the fair and were raring to go with my campaign. We succeeded in lining up ten more coffees and recruited volunteers to work at the polls, help with mailings and deliver my literature door-to-door. People also came with checkbooks. It was unbelievable.

Until today Joan was the only Republican I knew in her township, but now I have a wealth of workers and supporters.

Chapter Eleven

September 8, 1976

My champagne brunch was fantastic. I couldn't have dreamed up a more elegant affair—a beautiful ballroom, a delicious meal, and lots of well-wishers. It didn't begin until noon so people had a chance to go to church. Mother, beaming all over, arrived with her friends shortly after noon. I think she's getting into the swing of my campaign.

A champagne brunch on Sunday was *not* Mother's idea of how to spend Sunday. Sundays were a day for church, family, and friends; certainly not a day for movies, cards, or frivolous activities. But Sundays were the only time the ballroom was available. At first Mother said she wasn't coming but when her friends heard about the brunch, they immediately ordered tickets. So, of course, Mother had to come, too. When I made my speech, I could see her pride and also her concern lest I say something she disapproved of.

At one point during the brunch my mailing chairperson, Gwen, went over to Mother's table.

"We're having a party to address and stamp Helen's literature. It'll be at my house October 1, and I thought maybe you'd like to help, Mrs. Wright."

"Oh, I don't know," answered Mother, but before she could decline, some of her friends sitting close by, asked if they could come.

"Sure," responded Gwen. "That'll be great. The party is all day from nine to four, lunch included. Come when you can and leave when you must."

"Something like Good Friday services," said Mother, smiling. When Gwen looked confused, Mother added, "but you're too young to know about that."

"I guess," Gwen responded vaguely. "See you then."

September 28, 1976

Such busy days. I can hardly find time to write, but I want to try to remember everything that's happening.

Now that her children are back in school, Marcie, one of Joan's friends, showed me around her neighborhood and introduced me to her neighbors. If no one was home, we stuck my flyer in the door.

After campaigning in her neighborhood in the early afternoon, we drove to a nearby area where many new homes had recently been constructed. School was over for the day and children were gathered in small clusters playing ball and jumping rope.

"Hi, kids," I called. "Would you like any of these?" I showed them a long narrow box containing pencils, bumper stickers, combs, and emery boards all with "Elect Helen Humphreys" printed on them.

"Can we have one of each?" a little boy asked.

"How about taking just one, any one you want," answered Marcie.

Before long, we had about twenty children gathered around, each one choosing something I hoped would remind their parents of my candidacy. Of course, we also went to each home and introduced ourselves to whoever opened the door.

One of the mothers had been watching us from the front steps. She said they have an arrangement where a mother is always on watch for strangers in the neighborhood.

"You can't be too careful these days," she commented. I agreed but find it terribly distressful that children have to be protected from all strangers.

October 4, 1976

At times I have three events in one day and by the time I go to bed I'm so tired of hearing myself talk, I often wonder if I make sense.

I usually begin with a recital of my past seven years on the school board:

"I've served on the school board for seven years and I believe my experiences have given me a good grasp of government. You probably know I've taken great care to hold down school expenditures and to keep taxes at a minimum. Much of the time we hear school officials blame Harrisburg for their financial and administrative woes, so I want to go there to see how I can help keep a balance between state and local government."

Occasionally Howard attends an evening function where other men will be present. One such time he would have been happier had he remained at home. At this particular coffee, a retired man owning a large property stood up. Before he even began speaking, he pointed his finger at me and jutting out his jaw, began:

"It's not right for you people on the school board to continue levying the property tax. It's totally unfair to us retired people. The amount of property I own has nothing to do with my ability to pay taxes and I think most people would agree with me."

He turned to people in the room and asked, "Don't you agree?"

He received some nods but mostly blank stares while people turned their eyes to me. I saw Howard fidgeting in his seat. We both knew this man was going to be a problem but taxation was one subject I knew well.

"There's no tax that's fair to everyone," I began. "Perhaps the property tax is a bit antiquated but it's all the state allows us to use at the moment. There's talk of permitting an income tax but as yet—"

"I don't mean income tax," he jumped in. "I think it should be a wage tax."

"Is it fair for working people to bear the greatest burden?" I asked, as I looked around at the others. "Many retirees have large incomes from investments and—"

"Wage tax. That's what I want. That's what they do in other states. Why can't you work on that if you get to Harrisburg?" And with that he sat down.

"I think some combination of taxes that does not impair the school district's ability to provide for educational needs would be fair and when I get to Harrisburg, I'll support and work for—"

"Sure, the school district will always get what it needs first, you can bet your bottom dollar on that," he spat out.

With that, Howard turned to the man and said, "You'd better watch how you talk, mister."

To my great relief, one of my workers, sensing this situation could only worsen, jumped up to ask my position on abortion, a safe topic with this pro-choice audience.

Following this change of subjects, the remainder of the evening went smoothly.

I try to be upbeat and fresh for each group, recalling the advice of a former congressman. "Remember, you have only one chance to make a good first impression."

October 11, 1976

I had the strangest phone call yesterday. Shortly after noon, just as we were sitting down to our Sunday dinner the phone rang.

"Oh-h-h," I moaned. "Barb, will you get that? Tell whoever it is we have company and I'll call back." We did have company—Mother.

Barb came to the table with a bewildered look.

"I can't believe that phone call. Some man for you, Mom. When I said you'd call later, he said, 'She can't.' Then he said, 'I never give out my phone number. I'll call back in an hour.'"

"Did he give his name?" I asked.

"Something like 'cornstalk,' but it can't be that."

"That's Mr. Comstock, I bet," laughed Howard. "He's a character. Come to think of it, I saw him on the street the other day and he said he was glad to hear you're running."

"I wonder what he wants," I said as we sat down at the table.

"Oh, that's right," responded Barb. "He said he wants to meet with you."

"Sounds fishy to me," said Mother. "I don't think you should meet with him, Helen. Why wouldn't he give his phone number?"

"He's strange," admitted Howard. "And if you do meet with him, you'd better make it in a public place. I can't imagine he's harmful but why don't you suggest the deli in the shopping center?"

So when Mr. Comstock called again, we agreed to meet today at two.

If I thought the phone call was unusual, the in-person meeting was an encounter the likes of which I have never had before.

It didn't take long to recognize Mr. Comstock. Howard had given me a good description—about eighty years old, straggly beard and a brown tweed hat. We sat in a booth and I ordered coffee, but he didn't want anything.

After the waitress plunked down my coffee, Mr. Comstock pulled from his pocket a photo of my opponent and proceeded to tell me what a wicked man he was, and that when he looks in the mirror each morning, he's looking at a crook.

But his real nastiness surfaced when he talked about my opponent's religion. Mr. Comstock could not abide Catholics and wished them all dead. His voice rose louder as he called the Pope a hypocrite, accusing him of having sex orgies as a young man. When I realized Mr. Comstock was half-crazed by his hatred for Catholics, I knew I had to separate myself from him as quickly as possible.

"I can't give you money," I heard him say as I was planning my escape, "but I'll tell everyone I know not to vote for that rascal."

"I appreciate your help, Mr. Comstock."

"And another thing," he began.

But before he could continue, I held up my hand and pointed to my watch.

"My goodness, I had no idea it was so late. I'm afraid I must be on my way," I said as I signaled the waitress. I quickly paid for my coffee and headed for the door with Mr. Comstock following.

Just outside the door, he pulled something from his coat pocket.

"You know what I have here?" he asked. And immediately he thrust a small pistol into view.

"Mr. Comstock, what are you doing?" I exclaimed, automatically putting my hands up.

"You're not scared, are you?" he asked with a big grin on his face.

"No, of course not," I responded, relieved to see him place the gun back in his pocket. "I just don't think it's a good idea for you to be seen brandishing a gun in public."

"Don't worry. I have a license," he tried to assure me. "I live alone in a wooded area near the county park. You never know who might be sneaking up on you, so I'm prepared. I even went to see Hastings, the D.A. He knows I carry a gun."

"I must be on my way, Mr. Comstock. It was good meeting you. Thanks for your help." As we parted, I felt my body give a huge sigh of relief.

When I shared this story with Howard, we both agreed Mother must never know about Mr. Comstock's gun.

October 19, 1976

Life is a series of coffees, wine and cheese parties, door knocking, newspaper interviews and, of course, the weekly campaign meeting.

Creativity never seems to cease with my campaign workers. One of them came up with the idea of a tote bag with the words "A woman's place is in the House—Elect Helen Humphreys." She ordered 200, which we began selling at cost two weeks ago. We have about ten remaining and are beginning to see the tote bags in the library, the hairdressers, the Y, and every place imaginable. What a wonderful idea.

But we have had some flops also. For some reason, when we chose the date for a fundraising square dance, we were unaware that the night coincided with the biggest football game of the year, the traditional battle between our local high school and its keenest rival. About six people other than committee members attended our event. The caller felt so sorry for us, he donated his time.

October 30, 1976

"Elect Helen Humphreys" lawn signs are popping up everywhere. When I met someone new to the area the other day, she assumed I was a very active realtor, plastering my signs in every neighborhood.

Several weeks ago, my volunteers had a sign-making party. They stapled two of my cardboard posters back to back and then onto a piece of wood shaped at the bottom like a spear, so as to slide easily into the ground. We take the signs to coffees hoping to find prospective sites.

We're all set with our newspaper ads. One is a full page ad with names of Republicans who support me. We have been collecting these names at coffees and wherever we have a few people together. The list now totals over 200.

We're reproducing the newspaper's endorsement to use for door-to-door distribution and as a quarter-page ad. It's great fun, but we're very busy—me, my workers, and their children.

One volunteer reported her pre-school child's comments as they set out in the car to do some last-minute literature distribution.

"No more Helen Humphreys, Mommy. Please, no more."

One sour note is the prediction of a columnist living in the southern part of the district. Among his predictions: "No question about it. The Republican candidate for State Representative in the 143rd District will win hands down over his Democratic housewife opponent."

November 1, 1976

I heard words today that seared themselves into my brain for all time.

I love door knocking in the trailer park. The homes are close together, many of them have lovely shrubs and flowers, there are no dogs, and I have grown to know a number of the residents. I look forward to seeing them every election and they appear to enjoy my visits.

I knocked on the door of Daniel and Emma Krause, an elderly couple who have lived there a long time. Daniel is the one who likes to talk about politics but today Emma greeted me, coming out of the trailer and quietly closing the door behind.

Emma's first words were, "We're sorry we won't be voting this year, Mrs. Humphreys. We so wanted to vote for you." She appeared thinner than usual.

"What's wrong, Mrs. Krause?" I asked, placing my hand on her shoulder.

"I guess you had no way of knowing but Daniel has cancer of the liver. He won't live much longer."

I hated to be selfish about needing every vote I could find, but after properly expressing sympathy, I asked if she would like absentee ballots for both of them.

"You can get us absentee ballots?" she asked, brightening up and standing a little taller.

"Yes. I'll be back later today with them."

"That will make Daniel so happy."

And then, shaking her head slowly, she uttered these words, "Young people today think they know what love is, Mrs. Humphreys. They have no idea."

Chapter Twelve

November 8, 1976 (Night before election)

I'm scared. My stomach was churning so much I could hardly eat today. I spent all day knocking on doors. Tomorrow Elaine and I will start out early to visit as many polling places as we can.

All I can do is pray, but I'm not sure it's appropriate to pray for winning an election. I guess I can pray that I'll behave properly whatever happens and that I can remember to thank all the people who have given so much to help me.

November 10, 1976 (Day after election)

Today has been unbelievable. The phone's been ringing every few minutes with congratulatory calls. I'm still trying to believe that I really won. I think the Republicans are also trying to comprehend what happened.

Yesterday was wonderful.

As in earlier elections, my workers—both Democrats and Republicans—were at every polling place urging people to vote for me. This being a presidential election year, many people came to the polls prepared to vote for president only, some not even realizing other elected offices were at stake, so having my own poll workers was all the more important.

For awhile last night, the results were grim. Howard, Barbara and I were at Democratic headquarters where Democrats from all over the county had gathered. Doug was at college. A large board continuously updated returns for the president, the legislative seats, and the congressional seat.

The local returns came in first. I was ahead. Then some of the outlying districts came in. I was behind. The vote seesawed over the next two hours, but finally, I pulled ahead for good. By eleven, all districts had reported and I had won by 853 votes out of almost 30,000 cast. I was ecstatic, as were my friends. The county chairman grabbed my hands and together we raised them in victory as the cameras clicked.

After all the congratulations and merry-making ended, we headed for our car. Once inside Barbara could hardly contain herself.

"Mom, that was a terrible experience. Every time he pulled ahead of you, I got sick at my stomach. I felt like leaving the room. It's masochistic to sit there and watch those returns come in. Don't you agree, Dad?"

"I sure do, Barbara. I don't know how your mom puts up with all this stuff."

Before going directly home, we went to Mother's apartment house. If her lights were still on, we would go in. Sure enough as we pulled up, her apartment was aglow. She was at the door as Howard, Barbara, and I hurried down the hallway.

"I knew it all along," she said, when we broke the good news. "With all those wonderful volunteers, how could you lose?"

I accepted her confidence, knowing it was ill-founded.

Mother's pleasure didn't last long. This morning she called as soon as her newspaper arrived.

"Why were you embracing that man?" she asked with a note of disgust in her voice. "That picture should have been of Howard and you."

I was taken aback by her comments. The headlines screamed, "Humphreys Wins In Big Upset!!" but all my mother saw was a photo of me with another man.

I calmed down enough to explain that the man in the photo was the county chairman who happened to be standing near me when the final results came in.

"I think you should have been standing near Howard and then he would have been in the picture with you, but I guess you weren't thinking," she responded.

I agreed and we hung up.

And now that it's all over, I'm scared. Scared of driving back and forth to Harrisburg, scared of meeting new people, scared I won't understand how the Legislature works, scared I can't do the job. I'm just plain scared. I still think of myself as a housewife whose main goal in life had been to marry, have children, and be active in church and community. So much for goal-setting.

November 21, 1976

Last night about 150 people helped me celebrate my victory at a local inn. Most of the people were volunteers who had worked very hard to make my victory possible. I couldn't have done it without them.

I almost forgot to mention the other election results. Jimmy Carter won and so did the Democratic congressional candidate from our area. Pennsylvania voters elected an overwhelming number of Democrats to the House of Representatives and a fair number to the Senate, thus giving Democrats a comfortable majority in both houses.

And, yes, the newspaper pundit who predicted my loss, called my victory "stunning."

Chapter Thirteen

December 3, 1976

I haven't been sworn in yet but yesterday I had a meeting with Governor Shapp. Constituents in one of my boroughs had asked me to try to set up a meeting to discuss a bypass planned for their area. I had no idea how easy it would be to see the governor.

But getting there was an adventure. The men had arranged for a private plane to take us to Harrisburg. As we were about to board the plane, the pilot asked each of us how much we weighed. We were all a little shaky about the trip when we heard those words, but to our surprise, the flight was enjoyable. It was fun looking down at Lancaster County farmlands and other familiar sights.

The governor and the secretary of transportation were quite agreeable and promised us the bypass would appear on the ten-year plan. I don't know how much that means, but my constituents were happy to hear the news.

We arrived home safely.

January 5, 1977

I'm home after my first day in the Legislature—Swearing-in Day. Howard, Barbara, and Doug came with me. First, we had to find my office. Not easy. Each set of elevators in the Capitol goes to a different section of the building and we, of course, chose the wrong one. Finally, we wended our way through narrow passages until we found room 606, only to discover I shared an office with four other legislators and two secretaries.

One of the legislators, a young man in his twenties came over to greet us as we entered the room.

"Hello Helen, I'm Ralph Harrington from Lehigh County. I've been dying to meet you. I'm a school director, too, and I've read all about you in our newspaper. I've staked out this desk for myself and I've been saving the one in front of me for you. Is that okay?"

"Sure," I responded. I hadn't even thought about where my desk would be. "It's nice to meet you, Ralph. I'm glad someone is looking out for me."

Within half an hour, we all headed for the House chamber, which was decorated with floral bouquets adorning most of the legislators' desks. I had none. My friends and I were unaware of this custom, and for some reason, the county Democratic organization either forgot me or did not think it necessary.

I loved sitting in my own leather chair in Pennsylvania's magnificent legislative chamber. At one point, I swiveled around to the back of the room. There my eyes leapt to the inscription ornamenting the rear wall. "And Ye Shall Know The Truth And The Truth Shall Make You Free."

For some unknown reason, the kick-the-can incident with the neighborhood big boys popped into my mind. Here I was—once again playing with the big boys. And then I posed the question to myself *Have you really succeeded in playing with the big boys, Helen, or are they just letting you sit in this wonderful chair until their friend comes back from lunch?* Time will tell.

After the opening prayer, House members were sworn in, using Bibles with our names engraved on them. The women's Bibles were white; the men's black, and they were ours to keep.

Following the swearing-in, Speaker Rafferty requested "the gentleman from Allegheny, Mr. Sanders," "the gentleman from Philadelphia, Mr. Beeman," and "the lady from Bucks, Mrs. Humphreys" to proceed to the Senate to escort the senators to the House. (I had received a special delivery letter two days earlier, advising me I would be an escort.) And thus a new session began.

Next came the parties—and what parties. Huge spreads had been prepared in each of the caucus rooms. Platters with all kinds of lunch meats and cheeses, potato salad, pasta salad, chicken salad, deviled eggs, cheese and crackers, shrimp, cakes, cookies, and liquor in abundance. It was quite an introduction to the Pennsylvania Legislature, not only for me but for Howard and our children.

January 19, 1977

My driving experiences have not been pleasant, but I am learning to manage. Several weeks ago, I made my first trip to Harrisburg—alone. Since someone had told me legislators can travel the turnpike free, I repeated these words to the toll collector as I reached the Harrisburg exit. The toll collector actually laughed out loud.

"Afraid not, lady," he said, hardly able to speak from laughing so much. "Someone's been pulling your leg."

I paid the toll and rode off, my face hot with embarrassment as I imagined the toll collector's enjoyment in telling his colleagues this story.

Then this week I had my first car trouble. In all my

worrying about driving back and forth to Harrisburg, I had totally neglected to think about nasty weather. The temperatures here in Harrisburg were in the single digits ten nights straight. My car is not up to these freezing nights and last night, whatever freezes in a car froze.

I went out to the motel parking lot this morning and discovered my car wouldn't start. Sam, another legislator in our office, checked out of the motel the same time I did, so he drove me to the Capitol.

Secretaries are wonderful. Mine called a mechanic friend who went to the motel, fixed something in my car and poured in enough antifreeze to hold me over until I return home. I think a new car is in the offing.

I'm beginning to feel more comfortable here and not quite so scared of all these new experiences. I have discovered in life that I always seem to find someone willing to help. I think these people are called "angels."

I've met several democratic woman legislators. We had dinner together the other night, and then one of them, Gladys, was in the motel dining room for breakfast. We sat together and chatted. She's from Erie and has four grown children, two of them married. This is her first term here, too, but she's been a township supervisor. She doesn't know how she's going to cope with the eight-hour drive each way, every week. And she misses her grandchildren.

I learned more about Sam, who shares our office and sits in front of me in the House chamber. He's from York County, is twenty-nine, single, and had a job fundraising for the Salvation Army. Many of these new Democrats are young, unmarried men.

February 3, 1977

We have a new car and I have my first big vote coming up next week. It's not an easy vote—for me and for many other Democrats.

The Speaker, a Democrat, has been indicted for accepting money from wealthy parents to secure admission to graduate school for their children. He has not yet had a trial. The Republicans want him to step down as Speaker on the grounds that an indicted person should not serve in such high office. The Democrats argue that he has not been found guilty so he should remain in office.

Since many of us new Democrats were elected, in part as a result of the Watergate backlash and voter disgust with other political shenanigans, we decided to meet last week to discuss our course of action. Twelve of us were there, including Sam and Gladys. Ralph had gone home. (He goes home almost every night.)

"We can't support influence-peddling, for God's sake," began Sam, after we had settled in with sodas and pretzels in one of the legislator's apartment.

"You're right," said Rod. "What would the people back home think if we voted to keep him as Speaker? All our Watergate bashing and talk about integrity in office wouldn't mean a hill of beans."

"Yeah, but I'm uneasy about going against the Speaker," said one of the men who came from a Democratic stronghold. "My people expect me to be a party man, down the line."

"Not on this, Jim, for God's sake. Where's your sense of right and wrong?" retorted Sam. "Come on, we all have to stand together, right?" he continued as he looked around at the rest of us.

"All right," agreed Jim, as he saw our heads nodding

in agreement. "I'll go with you guys, but if I lose my next election, I'll have your necks."

We left the apartment agreeing to support the motion requesting the Speaker to step down. None of us had yet experienced the strength of the leadership. As a matter of fact, the leaders knew about our meeting before we even arrived at the Capitol the next morning. So much for our secret meeting.

No sooner had I arrived home in Bucks County on Wednesday when the phone rang.

"I hate to tell you this, Helen, but I've got to support the Speaker," said the voice at the other end of the line. "Man, you can't believe the pressure back here. The party chairman called last night telling me a few nasty things—like no garbage collection in my district if I don't support the Speaker. That's tough, man. I can't do that to my people."

"Of course not," I managed to respond, amazed by the tactics used in big city politics. "I'm sorry you can't stick with us but I understand. Maybe some others will run into difficulties, too. See you next week."

"Thanks. You know I'm with you in spirit," Jim continued, "and there's just a chance someone will work out a compromise, don't you think?" he asked.

"Yeah, maybe," I answered, not really believing in such good fortune. "Don't worry. The others will understand. See you Monday," I said, trying to hang up.

"These guys are tough, Helen, let me tell you. You people out in the suburbs have no idea what it's like."

He was right.

February 8, 1977

Our bloc had been broken, not just by Jim but by other

legislators from strong Democratic areas. They had phone calls similar to his, although their threats were mostly in the form of denying support in future campaigns.

We voted yesterday. Most Republicans and suburban Democrats voted to request the Speaker to resign, but with an overwhelming Democrat membership in the House, the Speaker managed to hold on to office. We all headed home.

When I walked in the door last night, Howard handed me a special delivery letter from the Speaker. I was afraid to open it. We ate dinner and still the letter sat unopened. Howard said I was being silly. What could the Speaker do to me? I think he can do plenty but I'm not sure what.

Finally, I opened it. To my surprise, the Speaker was very gracious and said he understood why it had been necessary for me to vote as I had and said he looked forward to working with me in the future. Phew.

This morning, the lead editorial read "Congratulations to Mrs. Humphreys for her independent stand."

I guess I've weathered my first test.

Chapter Fourteen

March 21, 1977

I am becoming accustomed to the routine. Monday mornings I drive to Allentown where I meet Ralph and several other legislators for carpooling to Harrisburg. At 11 a.m., both Republicans and Democrats meet in caucus to review upcoming bills and other issues of interest. We learn the week's schedule and our probable adjournment for the week—usually Tuesday late in the day or sometime Wednesday.

I'm also learning a lesson about being with an overwhelming number of men on a regular basis. The atmosphere is such that these men have no regard for the presence of women, as opposed to the careful courtesy of the men on the school board. Incidents frequently occur to remind us we are in the minority. Gladys can't stand it.

Caucuses are particularly difficult. I can adjust to most of the crude language and the off-color jokes but when legislators turn to observe my reaction, I usually turn red. Just the other day, after a particularly crude remark, I walked to the water cooler in the back of the room. Another legislator joined me, and although I hardly knew him, I could sense his animosity.

"I have a bit of advice for you, Mrs. Humphreys." He spoke slowly as he shook his water cup at me with every few words. "You chose to invade our territory, you know, and you're going to have to learn to live with us. Understand?" he concluded, jutting out his chin with his last word.

He flipped his paper cup into the trashcan and gave one last nod before returning to his seat. I remained glued to the floor in astonishment. I felt like a small child, unable to speak to the voice of authority. I would love to have had an answer, but I still don't know what it would have been. I'm surprised that I feel intimidated by these men.

Committees meet every few weeks, depending on the immediacy of bills to be considered. Rarely do we know what bills will be discussed. I may have borrowed myself a little trouble in the Agriculture Committee last week over this issue.

It was our first meeting. When I arrived, several committee members were already seated around a large table, while legislative staff and lobbyists were chatting in small clusters. I found an empty seat at the table where a staffer had placed an agenda and a set of bills. I began looking over the material, none of which I had seen before.

After the chairman called us together, we proceeded to vote on each of the bills, with not one bit of discussion. I was astonished. I had no idea what I was voting on or why. Most of the committee members are farmers. Talk about conflict of interest. Of course, it's true that these men know much more about agricultural issues than I do, but I asked to be on this committee thinking I would receive help from the many farmers in my district and from professors at a local college offering degrees in agriculture-related fields.

But here's where I almost shot myself in the foot. The

chairman looked around the room, thanked us all, and called for a motion to adjourn.

I raised my hand. The chairman—with a frown on his face as if to say *What is this woman up to?*—granted me permission to speak.

"I was wondering if in the future we could have the agenda in advance of our meetings?" I asked. "I didn't know what we would be voting on today, and I would have liked to talk to someone from my district about these bills before voting on them."

I heard snickering from the lobbyists sitting around the edge of the room. Their beaming faces showed they were enjoying this challenge to the chairman from a freshman legislator. All eyes were on the chairman as he turned to one of the staff people and asked if it was possible to distribute agendas in advance. When the staffer nodded in the affirmative, the chairman banged his gavel and strode from the room, ignoring everyone in his path.

Later in the day, one of the lobbyists came to my room.

"Helen Humphreys, I'm pleased to meet you. Tom Whittaker here—represent the horse racing industry. You gave us quite a chuckle this morning. I've just come from the Speaker's office. His aide tells me when your request for an agenda reached the Speaker's ears, he roared with laughter. Keep up the good work." And off he went.

Why does a lobbyist for horse racing attend our agriculture committee meeting? I guess because racehorses live on farms.

Later in the day, Sam and some of my young legislator friends commented on my bravery, but Ralph didn't think it was so smart.

"They'll get you for that, you know," he warned.

Actually, I didn't think I had done anything wrong.

I knew how we worked on the school board and assumed that all public organizations had to give due notice of business to be discussed.

Ralph wasn't the only one who shared the viewpoint that I might have borrowed trouble. Gus, a senior legislator from my area, agreed. The next morning while we were on the floor of the House, he called me aside.

"You better not offend the old timers, Helen. Committee chairmen are powerful. They could use their influence to stand in the way of bills you may want to sponsor in the future, so watch your step.

"And another word of advice." He turned to see if anyone was close enough to hear our conversation. Lowering his voice, he continued, "Sometimes you may see things we don't want folks back home to know about. Personal things, you know. We just keep this information among ourselves. Okay?"

I didn't know what he was talking about, but I shrugged and indicated that was fine with me. Now that I know these guys are up to something, I'll be on the lookout.

April 18, 1977

I'm sitting in my hotel room, after having had dinner with the candy and tobacco lobbyists. Isn't that a strange combination—candy and tobacco? I guess you can get fat and develop cancer at the same time.

Almost every Monday night, some lobbying group entertains legislators. Unless I arrive early to the affair, all the good hors d'oeuvres are gone—especially the shrimp. I enjoy the events more when people from home are present. Last week, I sat with a group of men in the construction business. Their wives were also along and we all had a good time.

Since the dinner tonight was in the ballroom of this hotel, I made a reservation to stay here. If there's no special dinner, Gladys and I usually stay at a motel close to the Capitol. We eat together in the motel restaurant and then go to our separate rooms. Evenings can be very long and lonely, even though I always have a book and a deck of cards with me. Sometimes I answer mail while watching TV.

Every so often I eat with the young male Democratic legislators who work in the same suite with me. Since most of us share offices with three or more other legislators, it's easy to decide what time to eat and where to go—Dirty Sam's, Mom's Place or some such eating establishment. I enjoy being with them once in awhile, even though they are young enough to be my son. I thought I would be uncomfortable with them, but we usually talk about legislation, the leadership, and politics.

I think Elaine would love these political discussions. I'll ask her to come sometime soon.

May 13, 1977

Home for a few days.

I spoke to a women's group the other night. I had planned to talk about upcoming legislation effecting education, but right off the bat, one woman asked if I had always wanted to be in politics. So I changed my speech.

Of course, the answer is "no," but I thought it might be helpful if I said more about myself.

"My mother reports that when I was a child and people asked me what I wanted to be when I grew up, I would say, 'I don't want to be anything. I want to be just like my mother.'

"And, in truth, I did expect to be like my mother—wife, mother, active in church and volunteer activities. I had no intention of being a mother who went to the workplace every day.

"When our children were young, they kept me busy, as did my women's groups and church activities. But after the children were in school, an elementary school principal called to say he needed substitute teachers. Would I be interested? Could he send me an application to fill out? I said I wasn't interested, but in reality, I was scared to leave the security of my home. He persisted, so I accepted an invitation to visit his school, but only to observe. It was a wonderful experience. I liked meeting new people and simply being out of the house.

"Soon I was a substitute teacher, and continued to be so for several years until I found a part-time job directing crafts and social activities in a nursing home. My confidence continued to grow and when the opportunity to run for school board presented itself, I jumped in. My life changed dramatically."

After the meeting, the woman who asked about my interest in politics came up to me and said, "Thanks for sharing your fears about leaving your home and moving out into the world. That's where I am now, but as I sat listening to you, I said to myself *That woman's got her shit together. If she can do it, so can I.*"

I hadn't thought of my life that way.

Chapter Fifteen

June 8, 1977

I brought Elaine with me to Harrisburg last week. What a great time she had at dinner with my young male legislator friends. Since we are now in the midst of budget negotiations, our discussions were quite lively.

Two days ago we had a test vote on the proposed budget. The Democratic leadership is shy some thirty votes for approval. Most of us newer legislators think it's loaded with fat and won't even consider voting for it. But we are learning that the leadership has ways of making people reconsider.

Each day, some of us who voted "no" on the proposed budget are beckoned to appear in the office of the majority leader. Not knowing what to expect, we are somewhat apprehensive, but the sessions are fairly agreeable. The majority leader offers incentives to attempt to secure affirmative votes. Most of my friends have remained adamant in their opposition to the budget; however, one friend who had been through the process last year did change his vote.

"How come you changed your vote?" I asked. "Did they promise you something?"

"A traffic light at a busy intersection in my home town." He paused and laughing, he continued, "It's the same traffic light they promised last year." He didn't seem too upset. I think he's in a safe Democratic district.

Yesterday I received my phone call.

As I entered the majority leader's office, paneled with dark mahogany and outfitted with beautiful brass fixtures, I was kind of scared. I had never been there before and didn't know how to behave. Did I sit or wait for him to tell me to sit?

"I guess you know why you're here," he began, shuffling a pile of papers on his desk. "I know you intend to vote against the budget, but I was hoping we might give you something to help change your mind. Something you could take back home. Perhaps money for a museum or a park. Something like that."

"No," I said, shaking my head. "I just can't vote for an inflated budget."

"It isn't inflated, but okay," he said. "I had to give it a try." He nodded his head towards the door to excuse me. I was glad that interview was over. I never did sit down.

Now today I was called to another office. This time I met with one of the Governor's aides, a young man in his thirties who thought he could appeal to my softer side. I have trouble taking these young men seriously. I have to keep reminding myself that Thomas Jefferson was only thirty-three when he wrote the Declaration of Independence, albeit with help from seventy year old Benjamin Franklin.

"Don't you know, Helen, lots of poor people are going to suffer because you won't approve this budget?" he said, pushing his chair back from his desk revealing that he had kicked off his loafers. "If we don't have a budget by the end of the month, everything stops. Welfare checks won't go out, state employees won't receive their paychecks, all sorts of bad things will happen. You don't want to be responsible for that, do you?"

"I won't be responsible," I responded, having seated myself while he was lecturing. "You know as well as I do the budget is padded with lots of unnecessary items. It's not my fault if the budget isn't passed. You guys need to do some trimming."

He dismissed me by nodding toward the door. I took my time getting up. I didn't want this young guy who couldn't keep his shoes on to think he could intimidate me. My parting words were, "By the way, I am truly sorry that welfare checks won't go out."

This process of rounding up votes can be boring, but we have to stay in Harrisburg in case a special vote is called. There's not much to do since we have already answered our mail and have solved most of our constituents' problems. We spend time calling family and friends on our WATS line.

Yesterday Gladys and I took a walk along the Susquehanna. She doesn't like being here one bit, mainly because she has an eight-hour trip back and forth every week. Besides, these guys drive her nuts.

"How can you stand them?" she asked. I suggested it might be because I have older brothers and learned long ago that men are no smarter than women. And then, I told her what one of the black legislators had told me when I first came to Harrisburg.

"We know, don't we, Representative Humphreys, that all the brains in the world have not been bestowed on white males."

Gladys agreed, but said she's leaving here as soon as she can find something she would like to do close to home.

Sessions can be boring. Legislators often make speeches about why or why not we should vote for some amendment to the budget, all of which we have already heard in caucus. At one late evening session, I noticed one of my neighbors sipping bourbon and puffing on a cigar. He remained serene throughout the entire evening, while the rest of us moved about, talked with neighbors, went back to our offices for coffee or to phone home. It's difficult to concentrate late at night.

Daytime is easier. One legislator is working on a novel and another completed a sweater she's been knitting for her son. Others, including me, do crossword puzzles. I also attempt to solve those scrambled word puzzles, which I think are difficult. While I'm struggling to find the solution, the man who sits next to me looks over my shoulder briefly and tells me the answer. He didn't even go to college.

June 21, 1977

I can't believe how we behaved the other evening. Bear in mind, we're all bored to death, tired, and want to go home. It was close to midnight during a particularly dull period when I noticed paper clips flying through the air. One landed on me, so I sent it back. From then on, I was into the action.

Throwing paper clips wasn't enough. The next step was to create slingshots, shooting paper clips through the air with rubber bands and bouncing the clips off heads of legislators sitting in front of us. After a few minutes, the Speaker called for adjournment. Fortunately, the news reporters who were in the House that evening did not share the paper clip throwing caper with our constituents back home.

The worst part of the episode is what we learned the next day. The cleaning women had to pick up each paper clip by hand because the clips would have damaged the vacuum cleaners. How dreadful of us.

Our boredom is becoming worse and so is the mischief. Last night the water cooler in an adjoining room became empty.

"Who has some beer?" asked one of the fellows. Before I knew it, some of the fellows had poured cans of beer into the large bottle that sits on top of the cooler. At first, the beer poured freely, but abruptly the flow ceased. The dispenser was jammed beyond repair.

Someone is installing a new one right now.

June 28, 1977

I can blame the beer incident on the younger legislators, but yesterday I was irresponsible.

News reporters are as bored as we are. One of them sought me out for a story, which was unusual, since freshman legislators aren't usually interviewed. When he asked my impression of what was happening with the budget, I was unfortunately too frank. I said, "Since most of us can do nothing about this impasse, we sit around all day waiting to see what the leadership is going to do next. As a matter of fact, the leadership makes us look like a bunch of nincompoops."

Although many public officials claim they are not quoted accurately, I was quoted precisely this time. How horrible it was for me to read my words in the paper this morning. And now I've learned the reporter works for one of the news wires and the article is appearing statewide. I'm scared. I went too far in my criticism of the leadership. I cannot imagine what awaits me.

For now, some of the young guys in the office are calling me and each other nincompoops, but so far, no one in leadership has said a word to me. I trust I have learned a lesson.

July 6 1977

The budget passed July 3 at 4 a.m. Even though we had been awake all night, most of us headed home immediately. Because of the uncertain schedule during the last two weeks, those of us who usually rode together had chosen to have our own cars with us in Harrisburg. Therefore, I found myself driving home alone, dead tired, shortly after four in the morning. I can't believe I'm the same person who was afraid to drive alone twenty minutes to the vo-tech meetings.

The five of us who often traveled together formed a caravan of five cars heading east across Route 78. After stopping an hour outside Harrisburg for coffee and buns, we continued our journey east. As the other legislators exited in Allentown, we parted with honking horns and I continued my forty-five minute drive south, alone.

Close to six o'clock, about thirty minutes from home, I knew I was about to fall asleep. I spotted a donut shop with two cars parked in front.

When I tried to open the door, I found it locked. I knocked. A woman pointed to the clock on the wall. Five minutes before six. I kept knocking. Finally, she came to the door.

"We don't open until six."

"I'm sorry. I'm dead tired and am about to fall asleep standing here. I'm a legislator. We just passed the budget and—"

"Come in," she said. "The coffee's ready."

Oh, yes, as for the nincompoop incident, none of the leaders ever said a word about it.

August 17, 1977

Yesterday at the grocery store, while Mother and I were poking around the ice cream freezer looking for her favorite, rum raisin, one of her friends from church came by.

"You do know my daughter, don't you?" asked Mother, pulling herself up to her full size. "This is Helen, Helen Humphreys, my daughter. She's in the Pennsylvania Legislature, you know. She's in the House of Representatives—in Harrisburg. "

"Oh, yes," responded her friend. I wasn't sure what the "Oh, yes" meant but I was thrilled to see Mother's pleasure in introducing me.

Chapter Sixteen

September 14, 1977

I get so tired of being with men. Usually I'm either the only woman or one of two women at every committee meeting. We sit and listen to the men talk about fishing, baseball, horse racing, Penn State football, and a host of male-oriented topics before the business of the meeting takes place. Yesterday was different.

Jim, another House member, and I were dispatched to meet with the only woman senator. She was chairing a special committee investigating special education funding. We sat in her outer office about ten minutes before her secretary led us into the senator's office.

"I love your suit," she exclaimed, beaming at me as she indicated chairs for my colleague and me. "Did you buy it here?"

"Yes, at Jason's over at the Northgate Mall," I responded. "Have you ever been there?"

By now, Jim was doodling in his notebook while he crossed and uncrossed his legs.

"No," she said. "I do most of my shopping back home, but maybe I'll go over some evening when we're stuck in town. I've heard the secretaries talk about Jason's.

Reasonable prices, I understand."

"That's right," I nodded, secretly amused at Jim's discomfort.

"Sorry, Jim," said the senator, turning in his direction. "You don't mind a little women talk before we get down to business, do you?"

We then proceeded with the topic of our meeting, but Jim never did adjust to the flow of the meeting.

October 12, 1977

I've noticed that many legislators use little tape recorders to answer mail, even composing letters while driving to Harrisburg. I thought I'd try the same

Up until now, I had attached a blank sheet to the front of constituents' letters and then written "thank you, etc." My secretary, Lois, knew how to finish the first paragraph. She also knew how to end the letter. The middle section was a direct response to the sender, in my own words. It was not a canned letter used by many legislators, giving the history of an issue, reviewing several possible solutions, and leaving you with the question as to what the legislator really believes. I responded to each letter as best I could.

I thought all was going along well with my new tape recorder procedure until this morning when Lois threw the latest round of letters into my "In" box. She just stood there until I looked up and noticed her rare, grumpy-looking expression.

"What's up, Lois?"

"Mrs. Humphreys, could you please jot down your answers like you used to? Nowadays your letters ramble all over the place and take two typewritten pages. *You've* even told me how important it is to keep messages to one page. It's impossible to keep your letters short when you babble into that tape recorder."

And then her final shot. "They're boring and they sound like political gobbledygook."

"Okay," I said. "Thank you. Too bad you can't say what's really on your mind."

We both laughed and I went back to longhand.

They say you can tell which of the Apostle Paul's letters were dictated and which he wrote himself. The dictated letters ramble.

November 8, 1977

One year away from the next general election and only six months to the primary. I must begin to think about my future. I guess I'll run, but I don't like the feeling that I'm not making the decision myself. It seems I'm expected to run and that's that. It makes me feel like I'm on a merry-go-round and can't get off.

Sometimes I can't stand this place.

Yesterday as I walked down the aisle to my seat near the front of the legislative chamber, I passed three or four groups of men standing close to the aisle, engaged in conversation. In each group, I heard constant use of foul language. "Fuck" seemed to be the favorite word.

What a stinking horrible place I said to myself. *What am I doing here? And why would I want to go through the aggravation of another strenuous campaign to come back to this?*

When I mentioned my observation about the terrible language to a legislator sitting near me, he responded, "You're right. When I'm back home, I wouldn't dream of talking the way I do here. I guess this place does something to you."

He's right. This place does do something to you and

you begin to like what it does. In spite of my complaining about the men and the language and the loneliness, I have become accustomed to this way of life—meetings and sessions during the day, working on constituents' problems, the attention of lobbyists, the dinners, the particular type of humor, and the feeling that I am a part of important decisions. Sometimes it seems my real life is here, in Harrisburg, and that I am just visiting when I go home.

Like last week, I went directly from work to a church supper at home to hear a missionary speak. Before Harrisburg I would have been interested, but that night I could hardly sit still. I shuffled my feet, sighed, and shifted my body positions until finally Howard asked if something was wrong. I didn't tell him, but yes, something was wrong. My mind was still on Harrisburg. It's not that I wasn't glad to be with Howard, but I couldn't seem to make the transition home.

However, once I am home a few days, home becomes the only place I want to be. I hate Monday mornings with the thought of going back to the capital. A couple weeks ago I was heading up the Northeast Extension when suddenly I slowed down and actually pulled the car off the road and sat there a few minutes. I wanted so badly to turn around and go home. I didn't, of course. I pulled the car back onto the highway to continue my journey west.

Sometimes, the gap between Harrisburg and home feels like a huge chasm with no way to cross from one to the other.

January 18, 1978

Last week my nephew was in town visiting my mother, his grandmother. He seemed interested in my experiences in government, so I asked him if he would like to go with me to Harrisburg for a couple days. Since he's in the Army, I suggested he might like to wear his uniform. He was hesitant, citing the anti-Vietnam War sentiment throughout the country.

"The legislators will love you in your uniform. Believe me," I said.

The first night, we attended a reception at the governor's home. Legislators gathered around my nephew, even telling him of their own war experiences. And the governor's wife fussed over him, showing great interest in his ribbons. I wasn't surprised at *his* reception, but I was surprised at the new way in which *I* was viewed, not only that evening, but also the next day when he was my guest in the House.

Immediately after he had been introduced as my nephew, a legislator I hardly knew came hurrying down the aisle to my desk.

"So he's your nephew, is he?" he asked. "I saw him last night at the reception but I hadn't realized he was with you. How come you never told us you had military in your family?"

Considering that the representative had never spoken to me before, I was taken aback, but soon more legislators came to my desk to congratulate me on my serviceman nephew. At first I couldn't understand what was happening, but then I realized that having a relative in the service had made *me* more acceptable, had made me more like them—like men. How disgusting that having a nephew in the service makes *me* acceptable.

February 22, 1978

Some days I am exhausted by the sheer weight of being

expected to be everything to everyone.

Along with our work in Harrisburg, our constituents expect us to attend every function imaginable at home. If we make an appearance, we are praised, but if we beg off, we are uncaring; and if we appear at events where we had not been invited, we are unwelcome. Although most people appreciate the opportunity to share their views with legislators, many others scoff at us for being that dirty word—"politicians."

But I'm beginning to learn some of the other legislators' tricks. One told me if you sit in the back of the room, you can duck out as soon as you're introduced. I hadn't even thought of that. Another told me he has his secretary telephone him fifteen minutes after a meeting begins to tell him he has an important call. He then apologizes and leaves.

I have just learned another of their tricks. Many legislators do not accept invitations back home while they're in Harrisburg. That would mean traveling home one evening and traveling back the next morning. I really don't mind doing this once in awhile, since that's another night I can be home with Howard.

So today when I received an invitation to a meeting of local township supervisors next Monday night, I accepted as long as we weren't in session over the dinner hour. Now the other guys from my area are mad at me since they had declined, saying they were needed in Harrisburg. They had hoped to alert me before I accepted. I guess they'll have to show up after all.

March 6, 1978

The first hour of my drive to Harrisburg this morning was difficult. Now that the snow is melting, fog blanketed the entire area. Except for oncoming headlights and the taillight from the car ahead, it was almost impossible to know where the road was. But the farther west I traveled, driving conditions improved.

Since several constituents had given me car license problems over the weekend, I called Mac, my contact in the Transportation Department, shortly after arrival. He was surprised to hear my voice.

"How did you make it out here this early? I heard fog had shut down the eastern part of the state."

"I managed, but, yes, it was scary," I admitted.

"Here's something you should always remember: **Never use your dim lights, not even in the fog. They're no damn good.**"

Chapter Seventeen

March 29, 1978

I'm a candidate. Everyone expected me to run and I am. We had the big county committee meeting the other evening where I was endorsed without any opposition. I'll handle the primary as before, going to the polls throughout the district, handing out my brochure to remind voters they can vote for me in the fall.

Meanwhile, the Republicans have three candidates running in the primary, including the one I beat last election.

Back in Harrisburg in the Agriculture Committee, we're arguing over whether or not it's humane to give "bute" (phenylbutazone) to racehorses that have sore or strained leg muscles. The SPCA and other animal rights organizations are fighting it, saying the horses could break a leg since they would be racing without the benefit of pain to slow them down. The owners say that's nonsense. I tend to agree with the animal rights groups. A few years back, I took "bute" myself for a painful hip.

In the Finance Committee, we're holding hearings all over the state on possible gambling in Pennsylvania. This week we are in Pittsburgh, staying at a hotel where, from my room, I can look down onto the Monangahela River and Fort Pitt (Fort Dusquesne during the French and Indian war). This afternoon I walked over to visit the fort museum where I learned the history of various battles. I have just returned from dinner at a hotel atop a steep hill where we could overlook Pittsburgh and see where the Monangahela and Allegheny rivers meet to become the Ohio River. It's spectacular. Next week we go to a resort in the Poconos.

A big vote will be coming up on the floor of the House within a month or so. The bill will create a new agency to deal exclusively with the elderly. I'm not so sure it's needed since the Department of Public Welfare handles these issues now. I think the new agency is all about creating patronage.

April 10, 1978

I've heard of dead people voting but I'd never heard it defended before today.

One of our members is under investigation for voter fraud plus a few other infractions because his brother owns an apartment house occupied by an unusually large number of registered voters. Upon close inspection, it was learned that some of the voters have phony names and others are dead.

At our caucus today, one legislator tried to encourage the rest of us to be sympathetic towards our fellow member under investigation. After a few short remarks, he closed with the words, "After all, which one of us has not done the same thing he's accused of?"

That question caught most of us completely off-guard. We howled. Our leader adjourned the caucus and, shortly thereafter, our colleague resigned from the House.

May 2, 1978

Last week I filled in for a sick member of Mother's bridge group. I'm accustomed to receiving advice from Mother's friends, both on my bridge game and on legislative matters.

"Helen, that new agency for old people—it's a crazy idea," announced Lydia, laying her cards face down on the table. "They should just give us the money instead of creating some new bureaucracy. The Department of Aging," she sneered. "Whoever heard of such a thing?"

"We all agree," said Irene, about to put a nonpareil in her mouth. "We discussed this the other day at canasta and decided we should tell you. You don't mind, do you?"

"Of course not. I need all the advice I can get," I replied as I, too, reached for some nonpareils. "I'm inclined to vote against the bill."

"That's what we wanted to hear," chimed in Rachel, as they all gathered up their cards and returned to the game.

May 23, 1978

I'm trying to be more available for Mother. She had a heart attack last week. While under medication, she babbled some family secrets. When I met her doctor the next morning, he said, "So you're the daughter they sent to college a Republican who came home a Democrat." Mother was appalled when she learned she had related this bit of news to the doctor.

I'm driving back and forth to Harrisburg every day, leaving home early in the morning and returning home mid-evening. I normally go straight to the hospital.

Last night was very foggy and traffic barely moved for

long stretches. Close to home the fog was unusually heavy, causing me to miss two turns and go several miles out of my way. I arrived at the hospital about ten, an hour-and-a-half past visiting hours. The nurse at Mother's station knew my situation.

"Go right in," she said, as I was about to apologize for the late hour. "She's still awake, waiting for you. We tried to tell her the roads were bad and that you might have stayed in Harrisburg, but she insisted you'd be here."

"I knew you'd come," were the first words out of Mother's mouth as I entered the room. Such faith in me.

June 8, 1978

Mother had come home from the hospital ten days ago and I assumed she was doing well, but she was sicker than I realized. She died last Friday, June second. Howard and I were at a Democratic dinner dance. While Howard and I were dancing, I noticed a state trooper enter the room and question someone standing near the door. When he came towards us, I felt a shiver.

"Representative Humphreys?" he asked. When I nodded he continued, "there's been an emergency and you're to call home. There's a phone near the door."

All I could think of was that one of our children had been in an automobile accident. But when Barbara answered the phone, she said something about Mother and the hospital. I said we would go directly there.

"It's too late," she sobbed.

I was in shock. As people came over to ask if everything was all right, I replied, "My mother just died." I said these words as though I were telling them what time it was.

It was a difficult few days, first trying to comprehend

my mother's death and then dealing with family and friends as we tried to comfort one another. But the business of the Legislature kept on going.

The vote creating the Department of Aging was scheduled for Tuesday, the day of Mother's funeral. That morning, as her friends came through the receiving line to offer condolences, they whispered, "Don't vote for that awful bill."

Following the funeral, a family lunch, and the burial, I drove to the Capitol, arriving late afternoon. I soon learned the vote creating the Department of Aging was scheduled for six. I had arrived in time to cast my "no" vote.

While I was walking down the aisle towards my seat, I was aware of loud talking coming from the balcony. I thought we had a group of elementary school children visiting but as I looked up, I saw the balcony filled with senior citizens who had been bussed from various large cities across the state. They carried signs reading, "We'll remember in November," and at one point they began chanting the words. The Speaker told them to be quiet or he would have them ejected.

After all the arguments were heard, the vote creating the Department of Aging was finally taken. [Votes in the House of Representatives are recorded on two large boards on either side of the chamber. As we click the switches on our desks, the boards light up, registering our positive (green) or negative (red) votes].

When the boards lit up, a mass of green lights interspersed with three red lights told the story. The Department of Aging was about to become a reality. I, of course, was one of the red lights. The other two negative votes were cast by Republicans, one who was not running again and the other who was considered the most conservative member of the House.

Before the votes were locked in, the majority leader walked up the aisle and stood close to my desk.

"Sure you don't want to change your vote?" he cautioned, knowing I had just come from my mother's funeral. "It could hurt in the next election, you know."

I shook my head as the voices of my mother and her friends drowned out any other thoughts.

Shortly after the vote, we adjourned.

As I was clearing up my papers to leave, a legislator who rarely spoke to me stopped by my desk.

"All I can say is, you sure have balls." I hated his words then and I hate writing them today, but this, too, was part of my world.

His remark reminded me of an eighteenth-century forerunner of the feminist movement. Mary Astell, in a tract entitled, "The Christian Religion as Profess'd by a True Daughter of the Church of England," suggested the promotion of exceptional women to the status of "honorary men."

I fail to see why being an honorary man is a compliment.

As they were leaving, other legislators spoke to me as they passed my desk, mainly to offer sympathy on my mother's death. I gathered up my few belongings and returned to my office where my young friends were preparing to leave for dinner.

"Want to join us at Mom's Place, Helen?" asked Sam as they headed towards the door.

All I could do was shake my head. I felt terribly alone. When I called Howard at home, no one was there. I realized he and our children were probably at my brother's house along with other family members. I called my brother's house, but Howard and the children had just left to go home. I had to talk to someone right then, but who?

In my terrible loneliness, I decided to call my childhood friend now living in Connecticut. As soon as she answered the phone, I broke down sobbing. She had known my mother well, and she comforted me as best as she could at a distance of several hundred miles.

That night—the night of my mother's funeral—was the loneliest night of my life.

Chapter Eighteen

July 10, 1978

We passed the budget on time—almost. Near midnight on June 30, the legal requirement for the state to have a budget, time stopped. Yes, time actually stopped in the Pennsylvania House of Representatives for one full hour when the leadership gave orders to stop the clock. The hands ceased moving and we gave ourselves one more hour to accomplish our work. Fortunately, it was not necessary to change all 225 mahogany clocks in the Capitol.

We're back in Harrisburg to clean up a few odds and ends before summer break, and I'm in my motel room, about ready for bed, but I absolutely must write about today's major constituent problem and its solution.

My working day began at seven-thirty with a telephone call from an irate constituent. He apologized for the early hour, but said he was so upset he had to call.

On his way to work, he'd witnessed a near-fatal accident at an intersection of a major highway. The grass had grown so tall that drivers coming off the side street couldn't see clearly to cross. As the car in front of him pulled out, the sound of screeching brakes was terrifying, as an oncoming car barely missed crashing into it.

"Someone is going to be killed," he said. "You have to get that grass cut—now."

I was about to suggest he notify the local officials but he continued.

"It's your property, you know. It belongs to the state. You should be able to do something. I tell you, that intersection is an accident waiting to happen."

"I'll see what I can do," I responded, but with little hope.

"I know. I know. There's little you can do," he continued, backing down from his original gruff voice, "but I just had to let out steam."

After he hung up I called Mac in the Department of Transportation.

"The contractors are way behind," he explained. "We fine them $100 a day and there's nothing more we can do. They tell me some of their equipment broke down, so that's how it is. You'll just have to tell your constituent to be patient. I know how much you love doing that," he added with a hint of sarcasm.

Since I wasn't happy about having to share the dismal information about broken equipment with my constituent, I let the matter ride the rest of the day, promising myself I would call in the late afternoon. And then, I totally forgot until it was too late to reach him at his office. I decided I would call first thing in the morning.

Just as I was about to leave my office at six-thirty, the phone rang.

"Is this Helen Humphreys?" the voice called out impatiently.

I shuddered when I recognized the voice. I considered saying that Helen had left for the day, but I had no choice but to acknowledge that I, indeed, was Helen.

"I called this morning to complain about the tall

grass. Remember?"

"Yes," I said. "I was going to call tomorrow morning to explain—"

"You're the greatest. I can't believe it. The grass is cut. When I called this morning I didn't for one minute think you could do anything. I was just sounding off."

I was as shocked as he was that the grass was cut, but before I could respond, he continued.

"How about if my wife and I give a wine and cheese party for you some Sunday afternoon? You could use more visibility with our neighbors."

"That'd be great." I answered, barely able to contain myself. "I'll be in touch to set up a date. Thanks."

You just never know.

It's amazing to me why people decide to vote for certain candidates. One of my neighbors told me how wonderful our senator is because he comes to all the Eagle Scout presentations. And one of my constituents is now my loyal supporter because I straightened out a complicated auto registration problem, which was actually solved by Mac.

And I now have the insurance liaison in my camp. After she helped me with a constituent problem, I called to thank her. She said I was the first legislator ever to do so. As a result, she plans to persuade her relatives living in my district to vote for me.

August 9, 1978

Today was a bad day. I decided to spend an hour this morning trying to register voters at a local retirement home. I've visited people there many times and assumed I'd be welcome. As a matter of fact, I had called yesterday to see where I should set up my material and I was told to use the desk outside the dining room.

As I was setting up my materials, an administrator came flying out of her office.

"I must ask you to leave. Right now. We don't allow politicians on the property without prior approval so please gather your things and leave the grounds. Now."

Wow, that was a blast out of hell.

She waved her arms about as if to shoo me out like a chicken. I stood there amazed, blinking my eyes and trying to figure out what I had done wrong.

"Get out," she began screaming. "You must leave now."

"Whoa!" I said, trying to slow down whatever was happening. "I did have prior approval. I called yesterday and was told to set up my things here, at this desk."

"Whoever gave you those instructions was acting without authority. Leave now."

I could do nothing but acquiesce to her request, assuming the policy applied equally to Democrats and Republicans.

But I was wrong. Just as I arrived home, I received an urgent phone call from a Democratic resident at the retirement home. He said a Republican committeewoman was there that very minute registering people. I was furious. Feeling the blood rush to my head, I grabbed my jacket and keys and darted out the door.

I arrived at the retirement home just as Eleanor Dickinson, the Republican committeewoman, was walking down the entrance ramp.

"What the hell are you doing here?" I stormed.

"My goodness, Helen. I've never heard you swear before. What's wrong?" she asked, a slight smirk on her face.

"You know damn well what's wrong," I growled.

"I'm just registering voters," she replied patting her briefcase. "Ten new Republicans. Pretty good, don't you think?"

Really angry now, I pushed past her and charged into the director's outer office. His secretary told me he was in conference and was not able to see me. Ignoring her words, I went straight into his office where I found him watching a Phillies game.

"I'm furious," I began.

"So I see," he replied, turning off the TV. "What's the problem?"

I explained about my being banished from the premises while Eleanor was allowed to register people.

"We can't allow politicians here, Helen," he said. "I can't imagine who told you it was okay. I suspect Eleanor slipped in without anyone knowing."

I just glared at him, not believing a word. Realizing I had nothing to gain by remaining in his office, I stormed out past his secretary, who was shaking her head in disbelief at my behavior.

I arrived home so angry I was unable to speak. Howard and Barbara put down their coffee cups and stared at me.

"What's wrong?" asked Howard in alarm.

I just stared straight ahead.

"Did you have an accident?" he asked, grabbing hold of my shoulders.

I shook my head while he and Barbara shot puzzled looks at each other.

"Can't you say something?" Howard pleaded.

Finally Barbara decided on a different approach.

"Having trouble expressing ourselves, are we, Mom?" she asked. Her words finally brought a slight smile to my face and unlocked my voice. I poured out my story. I'm exhausted thinking about it.

I am so tired of fighting with people. I like a good fight once in awhile, but I seem to be facing situations that overwhelm me.

Chapter Nineteen

September 6, 1978

My campaign committee is again meeting regularly. This year, along with my personal letter requesting money, we're enclosing a tan envelope addressed to the Helen Humphreys Campaign Committee. I love to see those tan envelopes in my mailbox. How disappointed I am when the mail arrives without one. I hate my money-hungry attitude, but that's how candidates become.

Last Tuesday, I received a call at lunchtime and decided to let the answering machine take it. I wasn't in the mood for talking.

Suddenly my mood changed. The voice on the other end began, "This is Jack Bland. Our company's political action committee wants to make a campaign contribution and—"

Before he could finish his sentence, I was on the phone telling him how to write the check.

I try not to take cash unless it comes in small amounts at coffees, but when the cash comes in the form of one hundred and two hundred dollar bills, it's difficult to turn down. As a matter of fact, I don't, even though I feel guilty.

I do know enough to return illegal checks. The other day, I received one for $500 drawn from a company account. This is forbidden under federal campaign laws. In returning the check I suggested the donor might wish to replace the returned check with a personal one. He did not wish to.

I have received checks which I knew were funneled through one individual but given by someone who didn't want to be identified. I accept these. Is it wrong? I guess so.

As much protesting as politicians do about not being influenced by contributors, they're lying. Since even small contributions make me feel more kindly toward the donor, I cannot imagine what the depth of my gratitude would be toward a $5,000 contributor. Monetary gifts do guarantee access to my office, but I like to think that money doesn't influence my votes.

Last week, the lobbyist for an organization that had given me $500 in the last election came into my office. He wanted my affirmative vote on a particular bill, which I had intended to support anyway, but he began the conversation this way.

"Helen, you know we gave you a nice contribution last year and would like to do so again, but we may have to rethink our position if you can't support this bill."

I saw red. I was furious. Who did he think he was to assume my vote was for sale?

"Tom, if I ever hear you say those words again, I swear I'll kick you out of my office—for good. You have no right to come in here and threaten me. And I can live without your lousy money."

He blinked, dumbstruck as I continued.

"Now get this straight. I will always listen to your arguments and if I agree, I'll vote with you. If I don't, I won't. Is that clear?"

"Yes, I think you've made yourself perfectly clear, Helen. Now can I explain this bill to you—please?"

"You can, yes. But since I'm voting with you anyway, why don't you spend your time with someone who's undecided?"

Tom came back the next day, all smiles. His bill had passed in the House. He thanked me for my vote and also told me he had given a lot of thought to my comments.

"You were right, Helen, I had no right to come into your office and threaten you. Thanks for the advice. I shouldn't talk to any legislator that way."

October 5, 1978

Today my brother, a Methodist minister, gave the prayer in the House. I had told him in advance that not many people would show up.

I met him in the rotunda of the Capitol at nine. Since the House wasn't scheduled to convene until ten, we had a cup of coffee in the basement snack bar. There he told me something about our mother I had never known.

"Shortly after you announced you were running for the school board, Mother called me on the phone. She was quite upset. You know she didn't think much of women in politics," he said.

"I know. She told me every time I was a candidate, but she seems to have come around."

"Yes," he continued, "but that day, she was really upset, even angry. Here's what she said, 'Thank goodness, my last name is different from Helen's. No one here in the apartment house will ever know she's my daughter.'"

I was shocked and saddened. I knew she had problems with my running for office but I had no idea I had caused her so much embarrassment.

"I'm sorry," I responded, " but you do know, don't you, in my last election, she carried my brochure door-to-door in her apartment house, telling people I was her daughter and asking them to vote for me."

"She did know how to roll with the punches, didn't she?" was his comment before we headed up to the House chamber where the Speaker was at the podium, shuffling papers. He would be the one to introduce my brother. They chatted awhile and then sat down to await the entry of the mace, indicating that the House was in session. I ran to my office to get some of my friends to come to the House floor, but they were all making telephone calls.

I flew back just as the Speaker banged the gavel. He introduced my brother who gave the prayer to about ten legislators. We then recited the pledge of allegiance after which the Speaker shook my brother's hand, thus dismissing him before continuing with the routine business of the House.

"You were right," said my brother as I ushered him out of the chamber. "Is this what it's like every day? Just a few people show up?"

"Yep," I responded, "and, guess what. I don't usually come. You're the only reason I'm here today. For the next fifteen minutes, the Speaker reads bills that have been introduced and bills the Senate has sent over to the House, and other boring House business. If we really thought the prayer was important, I guess we should have it right before we begin deliberations."

"It was hardly worth the two-hour drive out, was it?" he said.

"You can tell your congregation that you gave the prayer in the Pennsylvania House of Representatives," I responded. "Maybe they'll be impressed."

October 25, 1978

Elaine was on the phone this morning. She's hearing complaints about my stand on various issues.

"You know, the pro-life people are really campaigning against you. They even placed flyers on cars in the Catholic church parking lot on Sunday, urging people not to vote for you. And a number of your Republican supporters think you're too soft on welfare recipients."

"I know, Elaine, I can't be someone I'm not," I responded. "You heard the committee people complaining at the meeting the other night. They think I vote with the Republicans too often. Do they think I can get elected without Republican votes? Anyway, I agree with Republicans on many issues, so that's how I vote.

"And did you hear about the teachers?" I continued. "They're up in arms because I didn't support more funds for our local school districts. I try to fudge when I can, but there are some issues I have to be blunt about. I don't know what else to do."

"I'm worried, that's all," said Elaine. "I'm afraid if these groups get together, they could defeat you."

"If they do, they do," I sighed. "I'm sorry."

"Me, too," she said. " I guess all we can do is keep plugging away."

I hate trying to walk a tightrope. I would like to say everything that's on my mind. I would like to tell the pro-life people it would be helpful if they would adequately fund the children and their moms once the children are born. I would like to ask those Republicans who think I'm too lenient with welfare recipients how they would like living on a welfare check. To those Democrats who think I vote with Republicans too often, all I can say is "Tough. You wouldn't have a Democrat in the Legislature if I voted the way you wanted me to all the time." And the teachers know I voted for considerable amounts of money for education, but not to the extent they would like.

As much as I enjoy meeting people, shaking hands and attending coffees, I wish I could be who I am more often.

November 2, 1978

Doug went door knocking with me today. He took one side of the street and I took the other. At the end of the block, he crossed back, laughing.

"Some man refused your brochure, saying he would never vote for a Democrat or a woman. I said, 'Not even my mom?' He laughed but he still wouldn't take your literature."

November 9, 1978

I won, not exactly handily, but a win is a win. Unfortunately, many of my Democratic friends who came into office with me on the Watergate backlash, lost. Some people predicted that would be my fate also, but so far, I'm holding on.

Our poll workers created interest on election day with sandwich boards showing my name and lever number in red and blue running diagonally across a white background. Instead of handing out literature, the poll workers pointed to the sandwich board. People were amused.

I did have a bad scene, however. As usual, Elaine and I visited polling places throughout the district. When I arrived at one poll located in a small community-owned building, I was startled to see a mural stretching the entire length of the building. Printed with bright markers were the words, "Helen Humphreys doesn't give a hoot about senior citizens." These words greeted every person arriving to vote.

I was furious. Using language I had picked up from young children during my days as a Head Start volunteer, I yanked at the sign, tearing wide strips from the wall. Elaine was appalled, first at the sign and then at my furious eruption into uncharacteristic language. She maneuvered me to the car as quickly as possible before I could do any more damage, and we took off.

The next day, one of my supporters told me that my opponents' workers taped the sign together. Then my volunteers tore it down. The two parties kept at it until the sign was damaged beyond repair. But the story of my tirade did not die and continued to be reported throughout the day.

You know, I really am a good-natured person, but this life in politics is making me feel angry far more often than I care to admit.

December 5, 1978

The usual male camaraderie took over today. It's customary on the Legislature's last day to allow retiring or defeated legislators to mount the podium for parting remarks. One man related the following:

"Being here with you guys has been the closest thing to being in the Army I've ever experienced. The great feeling of comradeship, the jokes, the meals together, the bachelor life, us guys just doing our thing. You're the greatest! I'll miss you all."

After he sat down, Sam, who had not been in the service, turned his chair toward me.

"That's outrageous. You might think this was a barracks," he said.

"Sometimes I think it is," I replied.

A little while later, he turned again.

"You know, I think our life here is more like a college dorm."

Neither analogy is relevant to my experience.

Chapter Twenty

January 24, 1979

Back to the grind of driving across Route 78 where there's always construction. We're usually exhausted after a day in the Legislature and feel like sinking back into our seats as we relax and leave the driving to the one responsible. All except Ralph. He talks and talks and is forever trying to engage us in conversation.

Here's what happened yesterday. Ralph was the driver and decided we should assess the day's activities.

"On a scale of one to ten, Helen, how would you rate today?" Ralph called to me in the back seat.

I felt as if I had been punched in the stomach. I was tired and didn't want to think about anything, particularly the Legislature. Just as I was going to say "zero," he continued.

"Actually, I thought that exchange about taxing golf courses was quite interesting. Didn't you?"

Before I could answer, the conversation was interrupted by the sound of a loud siren and a voice, seemingly inside our car, telling us to pull over. The flashing lights came next to our car as the state trooper beckoned Ralph to the side of the road.

"What'll I do?" asked Ralph, looking around at all of us as he pulled to the side of the road.

"Tell him we're legislators," said Max, who was sitting next to Ralph.

"I can't do that," exclaimed Ralph, turning to face Max. "You know that would be wrong. What if anyone got wind of this back home?"

"Just do it," shouted Rod from the back seat. "Do it, Ralph. Say we're legislators."

When the state trooper came to the car and asked for Ralph's license, he put forth his most humble self.

"We're awfully sorry, officer. You see, we're legislators and we've had a very difficult day."

The officer peered into the car, eyeing us all. Then he carried Ralph's license back to his car. After making a phone call, he returned.

"Sorry, sir," the officer said, as he returned Ralph's card. "For your own good, sir, you had better slow down. Have a good day."

"Thank you, officer," replied Ralph, and off we went, first breathing a huge sigh of relief and then laughing at how easy it had been. It's not right, though, is it?

I still don't understand how that state trooper made his voice sound as if it was right in the car with us.

February 6, 1979

We heard a message over the intercom today requesting all legislators to report immediately to their respective caucuses to discuss an important matter. I couldn't imagine what it was, but as we approached our caucus room one of the old-timers said, "We're discussing salary increases today. If we do it early in the session, the voters forget by election time."

He was right. Later the same day, legislators in both houses approved the raise. Many of us voted "no," but it passed. I must admit, I'll be happy to receive the raise.

I'm beginning to learn the meaning of certain phrases. "A very important matter" means salary increase. "The voting machines are not working today" means the leadership does not have the votes. "Trust me," uttered by our leader in caucus means we can all break into laughter.

I'm still not used to voting on the constitutionality of a bill. It seems to me that we should know if a proposed bill is constitutional; however, when we vote on the constitutionality of a bill, legislators usually vote "yes" if they support the bill or "no" if they're against it. If the bill passes in both houses, even though it's unconstitutional, it will surely end up in court.

This morning at eight I attended my prayer group. I guess I haven't mentioned it before, but last year I received a notice that a prayer group meets regularly on Tuesday mornings when the Legislature is in session. Would I like to attend? Yes, I thought I would.

I regularly join this small group of eight-to-ten men and women of different faiths, including a judge, a department head, a legislative assistant, a lobbyist, and several legislators. We use an inspirational booklet and take turns leading the group. I enjoy being with these people and welcome a reprieve from this hectic life.

Our intimate group is a far cry from the Annual Prayer Breakfast attended by a huge crowd including the governor, his staff, legislators, lobbyists, department heads, and, of course, television crews. What a phony show.

March 6, 1979

I had an unpleasant experience last night. One of the legislators was having a fundraiser here in Harrisburg and asked if I would attend. He said it would be fun—some light refreshments and a comedian. The cost was $100. It's early to begin fundraising for the next campaign, but since he's a friend and I had nothing else to do, I said okay.

About forty people, many of them lobbyists, attended the event, which took place in a side room of one of the local restaurants. When I entered, I quickly realized I was the only woman, in itself not surprising since this happens frequently. I sat near the front by myself, after greeting a few acquaintances.

The entertainer was a comedian from New York City who was supposed to be hilarious; however, as he moved into his routine I wasn't the only one surprised. He stood on the platform dressed in women's clothes and after a few warm-up jokes, began discarding one article of clothing after another, interspersing his undressing with jokes about the physical inconveniences common to women. At one point, he singled me out.

"You know what I'm talking about, don't you?" he asked. I merely shrugged and he continued his routine for another five minutes, but the applause grew weaker and the laughter more strained.

As he threw off his final garment and stood before us in jockey shorts, he growled, "I don't know if it's me or if it's you, but folks, this just ain't working. Hell, you can have your goddamned money back, for all I care. Good night!" He stormed off the stage.

"Sorry about that," said my friend, seeking me out immediately. "He was supposed to be funny. I had no idea."

"That's okay. You had no way of knowing," I answered, as I headed for fresh air, knowing my statement wasn't true. He could have researched the act in advance, but in truth, I think the men were more embarrassed than I was. I suspect if I hadn't been there, the comedian would have received much laughter, completed his routine with loud applause, and the men would have had a great night out with the guys. My friend's mistake was inviting me.

A few days later, he sent a letter of apology and a check for $100, which I tore up.

Other than that entertainment, evenings have been quite boring, a fact my friends at home wouldn't comprehend. I surely can't explain what I experience in the caucus week after week, nor will I tell them about the New York entertainer who made me feel violated. Nor will they understand how lobbyists bloom like flowers whenever we're in session.

For those people who think my life exciting and glamorous, they should see me tonight. As soon as I finish this entry, I'll be watching *The Mary Tyler Moore Show* while playing solitaire.

My friend Gladys resigned last month to become more active in local politics. I miss her, particularly at dinnertime. We enjoyed talking about our families as we sat in the motel dining room after a day with men. I can't blame her for leaving, but these lonely nights are now even lonelier.

March 30, 1979

Huge drama in Pennsylvania this past week. Two days ago, the nuclear power plant at Three Mile Island south of Harrisburg on the Susquehanna River had a meltdown, and there is fear radiation will escape into the atmosphere.

The Legislature closed and we all scooted out of town. My secretary Lois called me at home yesterday to say her family has left Harrisburg to stay with relatives in Maryland. She fears for her teenaged daughters' health.

It was an amazing day. Our office is across the hall from the room used for press conferences. Reporters had gathered in that area in anticipation of the appearance of Governor Thornburgh, who arrived mid-afternoon and attempted to calm the fears of Pennsylvanians, particularly those living in the immediate area. The press corps drifted in and out of our offices, using our telephones every so often. Federal nuclear authorities have assured Pennsylvanians that the reactor causing the problem has been shut down.

April 10, 1979

I almost fell asleep while driving yesterday. As a matter of fact, I did. This is the second time.

Yesterday I felt myself dozing off and awoke just in time to see myself headed for the middle of the road; the other time I was headed for the shoulder. It's such a strange sensation, because for some reason, my mind seems to give me permission to go to sleep.

Like yesterday, I was listening to music, and when the piece ended, it felt as though my mind said, "Okay, you can go to sleep now."

One friend told me in order to keep awake he takes peanuts and shells them while driving. I tried this only once and ended up with peanut shells and little flecks of red skins scattered all over the front seat.

Going to sleep while driving isn't the only hazard. This past winter we had some terrible snowstorms, rain, sleet, and icing conditions. So far, I have made out okay. No accidents.

April 24, 1979

We arrived yesterday to learn from our secretaries that Jane Fonda is due in Harrisburg for a peace rally. She has asked permission to appear before the Legislature to protest the reopening of Three Mile Island. Because of her vocal opposition to the Vietnam War, her request to speak to legislators is creating quite a dilemma. Many legislators are veterans, some having fought in Vietnam.

At our regular Monday caucus almost every legislator was present. The first topic was how we should react to Ms. Fonda's request to speak. As soon as the doors of the caucus room were closed, the opinions flew fast and furious.

"I wouldn't be found dead in the same room with her," spat out one legislator.

"She'll contaminate the House if we let her in," shouted another.

"Bring her on," said one young legislator, rolling his eyes and sporting a big grin. "As a matter of fact, I'd—"

"Never mind," responded the chairman, banging his gavel.

"I think we should let her come," said one of the women. "What harm can she do?"

"She doesn't deserve an audience. We should just tell that damn pinko to go back to Vietnam, where she belongs."

"Enough," shouted our chairman, banging his gavel again and again. "I'll see what the Republicans want to do and I'll let you know our decision later in the day. Now let's get down to business."

During our legislative session that afternoon, the anticipation of wondering whether or not we would see Jane Fonda hung heavily over the chamber. Finally, the Speaker said he had an announcement of concern to all of us, so we had better listen.

"Ms. Fonda will not be allowed to speak in the House chamber, however—" Cheers cut off the rest of his statement but finally order was restored.

"However," the Speaker continued, "she will visit in each caucus separately tomorrow morning. Those wishing to hear and see her may. The rest of you just stay away."

More grumbling occurred as the Speaker called for adjournment.

Over half our membership, including some grumblers, attended the caucus today and everyone was polite while she made her case against nuclear power. Additionally, since she was in the midst of making a film in which she portrayed a secretary, she visited our offices and chatted with the secretaries about their daily lives.

I like her. She used good judgement in the way she presented herself in the caucus, and she showed great warmth in communicating with the secretaries.

Chapter Twenty-one

May 9, 1979

I had a big day on the House floor yesterday. I don't usually have much to say, but I've sponsored a bill abolishing the State Board of Education. Although the House leadership doesn't support my bill, many legislators do, as do many school directors and superintendents across the state.

When the time came for me to debate the bill, I wondered who would be chosen to argue against me. Imagine my surprise when I saw a Republican woman rise to challenge my legislation. This woman rarely took part in any debates and never debated education issues.

I guess I shouldn't have been surprised since it appears to be a male thing to pit women against women. At any rate, when she stood up, the whole tenor of the room changed. You could see the men sit back in their chairs, getting ready to enjoy this catfight.

"Mr. Speaker," began Janet, "this piece of legislation is an affront to the whole education community. We all know the importance of the State Board of Education. They spend many hours each month researching the latest—"

And on and on she read from a text prepared by

someone else. When she finished, a number of the men applauded, cheered, and some even hollered, "Right on, Janet."

When I arose and went to the nearest microphone, other men cheered me on with such comments as "Give 'er hell," and "Don't let her get away with that, Helen."

I began, "Mr. Speaker, all the information I am receiving from local school boards and others in the education community supports this legislation. The State Board is an unwieldy group, appointed by the governor with no legislative oversight. They are responsible to no one and pass regulations, which place undue burdens on our local school districts and unnecessary taxes on our already over-taxed citizens. I urge my fellow legislators to vote `yes' for this bill."

Applause and cheers for me.

Then Janet was back on her feet to the accompaniment of loud encouragement from her supporters. As I looked around at the reaction of the men, I felt as though I was a contender in a women's wrestling match. I sat down refusing to debate further, knowing that everyone's vote had been decided in advance, as it is with most bills. Through some legislative maneuvering, my bill was tabled and I don't know if we will ever vote on it.

Over breakfast this morning, I told Barbara about the encounter. Her comment: "Gross!"

June 7 1979

At a Chamber of Commerce dinner last night, I sat next to a stranger. He and I shared where we lived, how many children we had and a few other miscellaneous matters, but the conversation never moved. He decided to lean around me to talk to Howard about work and the Phillies, who are on a winning streak.

After dinner came introductions. When I stood to be recognized, his eyes popped wide and his mouth flew open as he sat staring at this supposed housewife who does nothing of interest.

"You didn't mention you are a legislator," he said.

From that moment on, he made up for the time he had lost. He asked my opinion on various issues, but mostly he shared his problems as a small businessman.

Many times we become of interest to people depending on our career. I have a male friend who told me whenever he says he's a teacher, people skip on to another subject, but if he says he's a college professor, their eyes brighten as they question him about his field of study, where he teaches, and the makeup of his students.

June 26, 1979

The budget process is going well. I think the leadership is just a few votes short and will try to finish this week. So even if we're here for a long week, at least we won't be here during July.

When we stay past Wednesday you can sense the stress level increase among our secretaries. After the usual early week rush to answer mail and solve constituent problems, we legislators are at loose ends. We pester our secretaries to solve problems that have been sitting in our files for weeks, or we decide it's time to send a newsletter to constituents, anything to upset their normal routine, so they think. When we finally bid them goodbye, it seems as though the whole Capitol and everyone in it gives one great sigh of relief.

I sometimes wonder what it would be like if my secretary were to write her memoirs. It would go something like this.

"She needs this phone call made—immediately. She needs these ten letters out before the 4 p.m. mail deadline. She needs me to solve three constituent problems with the Department of Transportation. Her newsletter must go out next week and please find some clip art to dress it up. She's flying to the western part of the state and needs plane reservations.

"Also, if those banking lobbyists come to the office, tell them she is working on a deadline and can't see anyone. She heard the school superintendents are coming to town today and she doesn't want to talk to them either. If her husband calls, come get her off the floor."

That reminds me of the day I was in the rear of the House talking on the phone to a constituent when suddenly a page rushed up to inform those of us using phones that a vote was being taken. I quickly told the constituent I must hurry back to the floor.

"How come you'll be on the floor? Don't they have chairs for you?" he asked.

July 12, 1979

Yesterday, along with several other legislators, I attended the funeral of a colleague. As we entered the church, a ruddy-faced usher in his sixties welcomed us and told us to go to the side area where legislators were congregating. As I started in that direction he called to me.

"You can't go there. Only legislators. Wives must sit with the other mourners in these pews to the right."

"I'm a legislator," I said.

"You can't go there, just legislators," he responded, his voice rising a bit. "Right this way, Miss," again directing me to the public area.

"But I *am* a legislator," I repeated, trying to keep my voice down.

"My goodness," he chuckled. "What will you girls do next?"

People constantly find it difficult to believe a woman is a legislator. Often when Howard and I are together at functions, someone will introduce me to another person saying, "I want you to meet our state legislator." Before my name is even said, the friend reaches out to shake Howard's hand.

And I frequently receive mail addressed to "The Honorable Helen Humphreys" with the salutation, "Dear Sir."

Maybe it'll change someday.

Chapter Twenty-two

September 11, 1979

We've had a breather with the summer break, but attempting to solve problems for constituents never takes a vacation.

The big one this summer was helping senior citizens gain the necessary permits for a new building. The allotment of sewerage units in their municipality had been exhausted, but there are exceptions for special categories. After carefully studying the regulations, I discovered that health facilities are an exception, so I asked the administrator if there would be any health facilities in the building.

Well not exactly, she said. One room will have a set of scales in it. Hardly a health facility but I went to bat for them, using the health room as a possible exception.

It worked. The senior citizens have their sewerage allotments and also a healthy supply of money, thanks to the dozens of freshly baked cinnamon buns they've sold over the past few years.

And still the battle to build a bypass around one of our towns continues. I call the office of the secretary of transportation every few weeks in an attempt to keep the bypass on the state's ten-year plan. We now have a new secretary. The one I visited with constituents before I was sworn in, was killed in a plane crash a few weeks after our meeting.

I phoned the secretary last week. This morning at 7:45 he returned my call. I guess he was surprised I was in my office. At any rate, when I requested him to keep the bypass on the ten-year plan and move it ahead if possible, he reminded me of a bill he wants passed. I had been prepared to explain the reasons why the bypass was so important to the communities involved, but he cut me off.

"Tell me, are you planning to support the bill increasing the allowable weight of tractor trailers?"

When I said "yes," he assured me he would keep the bypass on the plan and even try to move it ahead.

I get tired of these games, but either I play or get out. So, I play.

October 15, 1979

Before I left Harrisburg last Wednesday, I had heard rumors of a rapist in downtown Harrisburg, but I hadn't thought about it again until my secretary thrust the newspaper in my face as I entered the office yesterday morning. The front-page headline read, "Rapist attacks again." He's reported to be a white man in his early twenties with long black hair, wearing a Penn State jacket. On Saturday he attacked an early morning jogger on the river path, and on Sunday he dragged a woman from the Market Street ATM into a side alley.

"You are not staying at that hotel on Market Street tonight, Mrs. Humphreys," Lois said. "They don't even have safety chains on the doors. I'm canceling your reservations and making other arrangements for you."

"Forget it, Lois" I responded. "I'll be all right. I've stayed at that hotel many times and I'm staying there tonight."

She pouted for awhile and then left the office. I soon realized she had spread word of my overnight accommodations to her friends. Secretaries from other offices made a point of stopping at my desk all day to try to convince me to move to another hotel. Since I refused, they offered other suggestions—push a chair under the doorknob, move the dresser in front of the door, or lock myself in the bathroom if I hear anything suspicious. I thanked them for their concern but insisted I would be fine.

Last night, lying in bed watching *I Love Lucy*, I had almost forgotten about the rapist until I heard a knock on the door.

"Room service," came a man's voice. I froze. I hadn't ordered room service.

Again, the knock and a man's voice announcing room service. I jumped out of bed and with a husky voice I managed to say, "I didn't order room service."

"This is room 424, isn't it?" he asked. "Oops, sorry, I'm on the wrong floor."

I flopped back onto the bed and lay there for ten minutes, listening to my heart thump. I was safe for now, but as a precaution, I pushed a chair under the doorknob.

This morning as I was about to go to breakfast, I reached for my key on the bureau where I always put it, but it wasn't there. I looked under papers, on the floor, in my pocketbook, everywhere. Still no key.

As I stepped into the hallway, I glanced at the doorknob. My key was in the lock—on the outside.

October 26, 1979

Was I ever on my high horse last night at a legislators' dinner in the lower part of the county. Since the lobbyist arranging the event had cleared the date many months in advance, we were all there along with our spouses.

Happy Hour was in full swing as laughter filled the room with small groups of people nibbling on pastry puffs, pigs in a blanket, and assorted hors d'oeuvres. Amid the laughter, the lobbyist's public relations director led the ten state legislators, our spouses, and a photographer from the ballroom into a small private room.

"Okay, your attention please," shouted the photographer as he closed the door behind him. "We have ten legislators and ten spouses. Is that correct?"

"Correct," called out one of the legislators.

"All right. You men stand behind these ten chairs and, ladies, you sit in front of your husbands."

I tapped the photographer on the arm and as he leaned his head towards me, I said, "I'm a legislator. I should stand."

"You can't," he said as he prodded the others into their designated places. "Just the legislators stand."

"But I told you. I'm a legislator."

"I don't care," he snapped. "It won't look right. You have to sit. Just the men should stand."

Rolling his eyes, he turned to the others and continued, "Let's see. You taller men stand here in the middle. And, ladies, once they're in place, you can sit down."

"I'm not sitting," I insisted as I stood off to the side glaring at the photographer with my arms crossed. "I'm a legislator. I should stand with the legislators."

As the others moved to their assigned places, they cast sideways glances toward Howard. Smiling at them he shrugged his shoulders and spread out his hands as if to say *Don't look at me. She'll do what she wants to do.*

I continued standing off to the side until finally the photographer growled, "Okay, okay, spoil the picture if you must. Stand over there between those two men."

When I took my place, the legislators who always greeted me with warm smiles and friendly comments during photographic sessions in Harrisburg, averted their eyes and kept some distance between themselves and me. The women folded their hands and stared straight ahead. For a moment the photographer dropped his head onto his chest and covered his face with his hands. Rousing himself, he looked up and nodded toward Howard to sit with the other spouses in front of me.

As Howard took his seat a hush fell over the group. The photographer moved behind his camera perched on a tripod, and tried in vain to make us smile. Finally, Howard broke the tension with the word "whiskey" and we all smiled. The photographer snapped his shot and we went back to the ballroom, a rather solemn lot.

December 5, 1979

My brother died unexpectedly last month—November 29, my father's birthday. His funeral, like my mother's, was on a Tuesday when I had to be in Harrisburg. This time when I arrived in the late afternoon, the House had been in session for several hours. I hoped I hadn't missed anything important.

But even before I sat down, I noticed something strange. My voting switch was open. That was odd. When we're absent, our switches are supposed to be locked so no one can record a vote against our wishes.

"How come my switch is open?" I called to Sam,

sitting directly in front of me.

"Oh, hi Helen," he said, looking over his shoulder. "How'd everything go? I wasn't sure when you were getting back." Before I could respond he busied himself with some papers on his desk.

"Why is my switch open, Sam?" I repeated a little louder, attracting the attention of surrounding legislators.

"U-h-h, the guys needed your vote for something," he called without turning around. I tapped him on his shoulder.

"Like what?" I asked, sensing something was wrong.

"I don't think you want to know," he said, swiveling his chair around to face me.

"Tell me, Sam. What did they vote me for?" I demanded as I felt the blood rising to my head.

"Okay, okay," he responded, moving his spread fingers up and down in an attempt to calm me down. "That bill about teachers having to live in the district where they teach."

"It wasn't that bill," I exclaimed. "Come on, Sam. They wouldn't dare vote me 'yes' on that bill. They know my opposition. They wouldn't dare do that," I said, shaking my head in disbelief.

Several rows of legislators had now turned their attention to our discussion. Mouths half open, they awaited Sam's response, slow in coming.

"'Fraid so," he responded, his face turning red as he squinted one eye. "I told them you'd be angry."

Angry? I was furious. I couldn't believe the leadership had the nerve to pull such a stunt the day of my brother's funeral. I marched down the aisle to where one of the leaders was sitting.

Leaning back in his chair, his legs crossed and his hands laced over his stomach, he said, "You look angry, Helen. What's the problem?"

"You know what the problem is," I blurted out. "What's the idea of voting me 'yes' for a bill you know I oppose? Didn't you know I was at my brother's funeral?"

With a broad smile, he responded, "We needed your vote." And he just sat there, grinning at me.

His grin and the manner in which he responded took the starch right out of me. My head drooping, I walked back to my leather chair. I was defeated and could think of no way to right the damage.

Perhaps I should have asked the Speaker to strike my vote, but I was too exhausted from the day's emotions. Rather than fight, I shoved my papers into my desk, and left the chamber, aware of the many sets of eyes focused on me. Bursting into my office, I immediately went to my desk and buried my head on my arms, like I did in second grade when I was denied recess because I had dropped my box of pegs on the floor. I tried to hold back the tears as my secretary offered sympathy on the death of my brother. She had yet to learn of the scene on the House floor.

Chapter Twenty-three

January 20, 1980

A big year for politicians—the presidential race. Unfortunately, our country is facing many problems, which have made Jimmy Carter a very unpopular president. Inflation is sky high, U. S. hostages are being held in Iran, and a feeling of helplessness has gripped the country. The gasoline shortage is causing long lines at the pumps and we are limited to five gallons at any one time.

I don't know how it will turn out, but talk is that Ronald Reagan will challenge Carter. This whole scene could be bad news for Democrats up for reelection.

I guess I'll run, but I feel like I did last time—that I'm on a track and can't get off, as if I have no say in the decision. Some days I don't like this life at all. I think of the freedom I would have at home, enjoying lunch with friends, working on genealogy, going to conventions with Howard, and being around when the children are home from college. But most days I think I can tolerate this life, even going so far as to think it's my responsibility to be here. And there are other days when I feel very good about myself, particularly when I'm able to help someone or some organization.

For instance, the other day I helped a family with the placement of their severely disabled child. The school district had told the parents their son would have to be moved to a different institution now that he was twelve years old. His mother thought he was doing well where he was, and she was afraid he would suffer considerably if he were forced to move. In spite of state regulations and through my intervention, the boy is now where the mother thinks he will continue to find a satisfying life.

And last week, my fire company legislation became law, thanks to help from some of my Republican colleagues. The bill allows fire companies to receive low-cost loans from the state to buy *used* fire equipment. Up until now, they could only borrow from the state for *new* equipment. Local fire fighters shared this problem with me, so I had the bill drawn up and secured co-sponsorship from other Bucks County House members.

But a senator stole my fire company bill and introduced it in the Senate under his name. My local Republican colleagues were furious and insisted on having my bill, with my name on it, as the one to be finally passed. The signing ceremony is in the governor's office tomorrow. I'll get another pen to join the one I received last month for my open space legislation.

I'm happy about my open space law. It was a lot of work. I haven't mentioned much about it, but I've been working for months with legal staff here at the Capitol and with a lawyer from home. The idea of the legislation is to allow municipalities to share allotments of high-density housing with neighboring municipalities, thus helping to preserve pockets of open space.

The idea came to me when I read an article by a Bucks County judge defending his opinion on an open space issue by saying his hands were bound by law. So now we have a law to allow more flexibility in saving open space.

The other Bucks County legislators, both Democrat and Republican, were very supportive as was the chairman of the Local Government Committee.

I wonder if this law will do anything in the battle to keep our state green. I imagine builders will find a way to circumvent the law, and municipalities will have difficulty working together, but it was worth a try.

February 11, 1980

It's good I attended my prayer group this morning. I hadn't realized I was in for a bombshell. I know some organizations want to see me defeated, but I had no idea I was a prime target. I guess I should have realized my vulnerability since I am the only Democrat to have ever held this seat and since I won both elections by slim majorities.

I learned how ugly the situation is today while standing in the well of the House waiting for the session to begin. A Republican colleague and I were discussing our past election antics. I told him about the time the Republicans placed the huge sign across the voting place and how I had ripped it into pieces.

"You've got a lot more to worry about this year than a sign across a building, Helen. You know you're at the top of the Republicans' list this year, don't you?" he said, smiling.

"What kind of list?" I asked.

"To be defeated, of course."

"Why? I vote with them much of the time."

"Yeah, but not when it counts. They need your vote for choosing the Speaker and naming committee chairmen. The Republicans want to be in the majority again. Besides, they think the seat belongs to them and that you've held it long enough," he responded.

I had heard enough and was about to return to my seat when he grabbed my arm with more bad news.

"And you know what else? You're also at the top of the teachers' shit list. How's that grab you?" he said with a big grin. "Both groups are throwing thousands of dollars into the race to defeat you."

I shook my head and walked up the aisle to my seat, wondering if I should really run again. An overwhelming registration deficit was one thing, but this intense effort to oust me from office was staggering. I felt my normal buoyancy flag.

Seated in my leather chair, involuntarily I cast my eyes to the rear wall of the chamber and read the words, "And Ye Shall Know The Truth And The Truth Shall Make You Free." The truth is—the big boys want their seat back.

March 12, 1980

Once again, I have no primary opposition but the Republicans have found a different person to run against me in the general election—a young fellow, ready to campaign vigorously. They really want their seat back.

And Jimmy Carter isn't helping any. It's too bad. I like the man, but under his leadership the country is in a mess. I'm afraid I may suffer from the Carter backlash this year, just as four years ago I profited from the Nixon backlash.

With the prospects of an unpleasant campaign, I'm on edge these days. I'm annoyed at the slightest thing. So far I have managed to keep calm in public, but I'm getting so tired of comments like "poor Howard," "Who's getting Howard's dinner tonight?" "I wouldn't let my wife run off to Harrisburg every week," and the real gem, "Howard must be a saint."

I would love to use some choice words in telling these people to mind their own business, but instead I try to explain that Howard and I have agreed on my pursuing a political life. Furthermore, and I don't say this, but if tomorrow Howard said he couldn't stand this life we are leading, I would quit immediately.

Actually, he has some good times associated with my work. Just last week, he came up with me to Harrisburg for a spouse reception given by the governor's wife. Of course, most of the spouses are women. As lunch was about to be served, he heard his name being called.

It was the governor's wife from across the room. "Here's your seat, Howard," she said. It was next to her. He's had great fun telling people at home about his luncheon with the governor's wife.

Not being the usual political couple makes our life different from many others. The typical female spouse often becomes intimately involved in her husband's campaign—attending all functions, speaking on his behalf, and organizing volunteers. Howard has his own life, but he occasionally stuffs and stamps envelopes, and he attends dinners, balls, candidates' nights, and other events.

When the Legislature is in session, before leaving for Harrisburg, I prepare food that will be easy for Howard to heat and, of course, I make sure the freezer has plenty of quick meals. Additionally, I always know he'll eat at least one good meal a week at Rotary. He seems to make out fine.

For awhile one problem annoyed me no end, but finally I had to let go. I hated coming home and finding dishes and pots and pans in cabinets where I had not left them. And when Barbara and Doug are home from college, it's even worse. I hate losing control of my kitchen, but I've finally learned to accept the fact that the location of pots and pans is a minor disruption in my life.

Chapter Twenty-four

April 11, 1980

Today I lost it. I'm sorry and I regret it. I went to the courthouse on voter registration business. Since the courthouse is controlled by Republicans, officially I'm the enemy, even though I have a number of friends working there.

As I approached the counter, a young clerk who had been sitting at her desk rose to help me. Behind her were ten clerks and secretaries busy at their desks. I showed her the papers I needed help with.

"I don't understand what you want," she said, shaking her head.

I explained once again, slowly raising my voice more than I had intended.

"I'm sorry, I don't think we can help you here. Perhaps you should go across the hall to the—"

Before she could finish her sentence, I went berserk.

"You'd sure help a Republican, wouldn't you?" I shouted as I grabbed my papers out of her hand. "Forget it."

Looking up at her face, I immediately regretted my

actions when I realized she was close to tears. I also felt ten sets of eyes glaring at me, telling me I was not welcome in their office again. I'm quite sure the story of my temper flare-up was repeated in offices all over the courthouse for days to come.

However, my suspicion about Democrats being treated differently from Republicans is not totally unfounded. After all, I was banned from that retirement home two years ago.

Constantly being in the public eye is not easy. Politicians are forever receiving criticism from the press, from opponents and from organizations that wish to see them defeated. Additionally, the opposing political party is constantly on the lookout for flaws—big and little—to use in the next election. I sure gave them one today, but I'd better settle down and try to recapture my sense of humor because the pressure is only going to increase in the days ahead.

May 17, 1980

Another bad political scene. Some of my supporters had invited me to a school fair where I was to meet them at the gate. We all entered the school grounds wearing "Vote for Helen Humphreys" pins. After I had greeted a few people, we noticed a small group of women gathered together, waving their hands about and walking towards us.

"You can't be here," one of them said. "No politicians allowed."

"Won't you even let a hungry legislator buy a pizza?" I asked.

"No, leave right now. You're just looking for votes. Go. You're not allowed here. Leave. Now."

"Can it be because you're a Republican

committeewoman and Helen's a Democrat?" asked one of my friends.

"No. Just leave—all of you. No politicians allowed."

By then we had attracted a good bit of attention. Someone in the crowd said, "Let her stay," while someone else said, "Make her go. She doesn't have any children here."

That person was right. I had no children in the school, so my friends and I left. Once again, I suspect I would have been welcome if I had been a Republican.

But last week was fun. I visited an elementary school. Young children ask such personal questions. "How old are you?" "Are your children upset because you are not home to cook dinner?" "Do you have to get dressed up or can you wear dungarees?" "Do you give out things when people come to visit you in your office?" "Does your husband work?" "How much money do you make?" And just before I left, they flocked around me asking for my autograph. Ah, fame.

June 17, 1980

Budget deliberations again, but since everyone is anxious to get out of here to campaign, approval should come quickly. None too quickly for some.

Just yesterday one of the legislators gave us all a welcome reprieve from the routine. I'll have to back up a bit.

On a Tuesday in February in the midst of a blast of cold arctic air, a legislator from Erie rose to say that his wife had called to report that the predicted snow had begun to fall. Dire road conditions were expected within a few hours. The legislator asked the Speaker to adjourn for the week so all those traveling to the western part of the state could head home before the highways became impassable. The request was granted, and we all went home.

Back to yesterday, a scorching hot day. As we were becoming bogged down in procedural debates, one of the legislators asked to be recognized.

"Mr. Speaker, I have just received a phone call from my wife. It's snowing in York County."

After a few minutes of comic relief we returned to the business at hand.

July 7, 1980

I did something brave yesterday. I attended the annual conference of the Pennsylvania State Education Association. Remember, I am at the top of their list. I probably was dumb to go, but since my local PSEA representatives had asked me to attend, I went. I did think people would be courteous to me and appreciate the fact that I had taken time to attend. Not so.

We legislators were seated together toward the rear of the auditorium. After the president opened the meeting the first order of business was to introduce us.

As each legislator's name was called, he stood to be recognized amidst generous applause. But when I stood up, only two or three handclaps could be heard, and those were from teachers back home. I tried to be amused by the incident but, in fact, I don't think I'll ever forget how much lack of applause can hurt.

I'm not sure why the teachers' organizations are so dead set against me. I know many rank-and-file teachers support me. Maybe the union leaders' list would go something like this:

• She's against teachers having the right to strike. My response: If police and fire fighters aren't permitted to strike, why should teachers? Isn't the education of our children just as important?

· She won't support the bill to insist that teachers live in the district where they work. My response: I never did understand why that matters to anyone. Don't we want the best teachers available to teach our children?

· She can't be counted on to approve increased appropriations for school districts. My response: Of course not. Not when some districts profit from a rich tax base, while others must scrounge for every penny in order to provide the most basic of educational skills.

August 26, 1980

My campaign committee is back in full swing, preparing for a race that could be my most difficult. I'll begin door knocking soon.

We've had one home event already—a Bloody Mary brunch. Someone else is planning an Irish Coffee next month. So much for the old morning coffees. No, I won't knock plain old coffees. They have produced lots of workers and have been the backbone of my campaigns and the main source of volunteers. Thank goodness for all those people willing to have coffees and for those people willing to come listen to me.

Last night was the exception to successful coffees. I didn't know the woman having the event, but she had called my office and said she would like to have a coffee for me. After I arrived, she and I chatted a bit as we waited for guests to arrive. Fifteen minutes passed, then twenty. I could hear her husband upstairs talking with the children. Finally her next-door neighbor rushed in saying she could only stay ten minutes.

The host and her neighbor advised me they were pro-life and they hoped I would support any legislation having to do with that issue. Since it's well known I'm pro-choice, I wondered why this woman invited me to her home. I guess she thought she and her friends could change my mind. I told them I respected their position but, of course, had to vote my own conscience. Then they asked me to support legislation banning secular humanism. I don't even know what they're talking about but said I would look into it.

With that, the neighbor departed leaving the hostess and me alone. After looking at the clock again, we decided to call it a night. I never did know why so few people attended but I suspect my hostess had waited until the last minute to invite guests; or possibly I was boycotted because of my pro-choice views.

Actually, I'm scared about this election. Republicans around the country are jubilant with the terrible state of affairs. They think they really have a shot at the presidency.

U. S. citizens have been held captives in Iran for over a year. An aborted helicopter attempt to gain their release in April set us into more despair. I remember the terrible sinking feeling I felt when I heard the news of the three helicopters crashing. I was on my way to a candidates' forum. What a dismal evening it was for Democrats, as the Republicans ranted on about the poor leadership guiding our country. I almost felt like agreeing with them.

Most upsetting to many people is our country's withdrawal from the Moscow Summer Olympics because Russia invaded Afghanistan. I don't know what's the right thing to do, but can you imagine the hopes and dreams of young athletes who have trained many years for this event?

All I can do is keep plugging away. If I win, I win; if I lose, I lose.

I don't mean that. I would hate to lose. I would rather resign. I can't stand the thought of losing. Let's hope I don't have to face that character test.

Chapter Twenty-five

September 9, 1980

I think everyone is becoming a little edgy. Maybe it's the upcoming election. Or maybe it's just that Democrats are on edge since the polls in general aren't looking good. Yesterday was an example of this edginess.

Aside from the day the majority leader came up the aisle to urge caution on my vote against the Department of Aging, he had never been to my seat again—until yesterday. We were voting to raise the minimum wage, an issue of great importance to Democrats and one I supported. I guess he didn't know I was with him on this issue.

"I hope you can vote with Democrats for a change," he snarled, as he stood glaring down at me. Legislators seated nearby turned to watch the encounter. Their eyes almost popped out of their heads when they heard my answer.

"I plan to," I replied. "And don't speak to me in that tone of voice."

As he strode back to his seat, other legislators shook their heads in disbelief.

"I can't believe you spoke to him that way," said Sam. "He'll get you for that."

I shrugged and tried to forget that I had been

disrespectful.

Ten minutes later and after the Democrats had won the vote, the leader returned to my seat. I hardly knew what to expect. Again, the legislators sitting nearby turned to listen.

"I'm sorry. I didn't mean to speak in that tone," he said. "We've had some difficult votes today which had me upset. I spoke too harshly. I'm sorry." He turned and walked back down the aisle.

I was so relieved, I could do nothing but sink into the comfort of my soft leather chair.

At the end of the session, the Republican women were waiting for me in the hallway.

"What did he say to you? We were scared, just watching," they clamored almost in unison.

"He just wanted to make sure he had my vote," I replied in an off-hand manner, as I headed for the elevator. I didn't feel like talking with Republicans about my encounter.

Actually, most times I am well treated by the leadership. I like them and I think they like me.

September 25, 1980

These last few weeks of campaigning have been depressing. First of all, door knocking when no one is home is exasperating. More mothers are working and others are out running around until five minutes before the school bus pulls up with their children. Then everyone is out the door within the next five minutes—for music lessons, dentist's appointments, whatever.

At our last weekly campaign meeting my manager Don said he has to have surgery and can't manage my campaign anymore. That was a punch in the stomach. I guess for him as well as for me, but now I have to find a new manager. Sometimes I think I could do it myself, but then I remember the saying, "He who is his own campaign manager, has a fool managing the campaign."

To top it off, we had a difficult candidates' night. I used to like them, but my opponent is better prepared than previous opponents. Not only is he prepared but his fans are ready with planted questions. For instance last night someone asked this one: "Who is your role model in politics?"

For goodness' sake. When have I ever thought of a role model? How many role models are there out there for women? There are no role models for women. I came up with the name of a former male senator as my role model, but this is one moment I wish I could live over. I would have said precisely this, "I have no role model, folks. Women have no one to help them, to turn to, from whom to seek advice. None, zippo, nada. That's why we need more women in politics." I probably would have been branded strident, harsh or unladylike.

October 22, 1980

As if we don't have enough important matters to discuss before we go home to campaign, now we have to take up smoking in the House chamber.

Two weeks ago, as we were about to adjourn, Representative Rose Everhart offered a resolution to forbid smoking on the floor of the House. A hush fell over the vast chamber. Such a resolution was not to be treated lightly. Legislators who had been standing at their desks gathering papers to make a hasty exit suddenly sat down. Quick thinking was necessary. Immediately, one of the smokers rose to be recognized.

"Mr. Speaker, on a matter of such magnitude to all of us here in this room and to the legislators who will follow in years to come, I move the resolution to forbid smoking be tabled."

When the Speaker called for a vote to table the motion, it was approved by loud yea's. We were all anxious to head home.

Then, this past Monday, Rose asked that her resolution be removed from the table. After several unsuccessful attempts to delay, arguments began.

"Mr. Speaker," began one of the smokers. "I would like to offer a compromise. It seems reasonable for those of us who want to smoke to confine our smoking to the rear of the chamber. We would not disturb non-smokers, and those of us who are smokers would be able to remain in the hall during important debates. I urge my fellow legislators to vote against the smoking ban."

Rose stood up.

"Mr. Speaker, smoking is not only a nuisance to non-smokers, it is destroying these magnificent works of art," she began, pointing to the rear of the chamber. "Look at George Washington and his troops at Valley Forge. You wouldn't want to destroy that, would you? And imagine what kind of film must be accumulating over the invaluable *Passage of the Hours* painting in the dome."

After turning to look at the Valley Forge painting, we all stretched our necks back as we looked again at the remarkable dome. The paintings are beautiful.

"We all know smoke produces a film on the walls in our own homes," she continued, "and I'm sure you have noticed the haze that hangs over this chamber, particularly on days when heated debates take place. We must protect this art for future generations. Mr. Speaker, I urge members to vote for this resolution. We must eliminate smoking from this chamber."

The debate continued for more than an hour and finally we voted. The non-smokers won. But that was not the end of the matter. Realizing that some of his fellow smokers were not in attendance, a legislator quickly rose to his feet asking for reconsideration of the vote.

Tuesday we voted again. This time the smokers won, but the battle was not over. After another reconsideration, we voted again today. The non-smokers won so the smokers gave up. Smoking is now banned from the House of Representatives, at least for this session, which is almost over.

October 29, 1980

Today was one of those crisp fall days that beckons a person outside. The Legislature is in session to finish up a few items before the election. Since we had a few hours between caucus and session, I decided to walk along the Susquehanna.

Out the front door of the Capitol and down the cascading steps, across Third Street, Second Street, and finally, Front Street, to the path along the river. Newly fallen leaves and crunchy dead ones lined the path. I hung close to the right side of the path, recalling the broken jaw a friend had suffered after being hit by a bicyclist on this path. No cyclists today, only a few walkers.

I wondered if this would be my last walk along the Susquehanna. Suddenly I realized I liked being here. I had grown to love Harrisburg. I loved the excitement of state government. I loved knowing people in power—the governor, cabinet heads, leaders in the Legislature. I loved walking the streets of Harrisburg and the halls of the Capitol. I don't want to lose.

November 3, 1980

I'm home, but in misery. Bursitis. I've been taking two aspirin every three hours, but I finally decided to see the doctor for a cortisone shot.

"Don't you have bursitis every election cycle?" he asked.

"I guess maybe it coincides, but this time it's awful."

"I think it's from shaking hands. Try holding your arm close to your body when you greet people. See if that helps," he advised.

I'll try to remember, but meanwhile I'm getting more scared than ever.

Do I fear omens? I don't know, but here's what I discovered when I arrived home from Harrisburg the other day. One of my campaign signs had had an untimely demise.

Early last month, as a joke, some supporters placed a large "Vote for Helen Humphreys" sign in the middle of a pond on Finney's property, located on a busy street. Fortunately the Finneys were amused. They also supported me and allowed the sign to remain. We were delighted with our strategically-placed sign and were ecstatic when the newspaper ran a photograph of it. We thought the sign would be safe throughout the remainder of the campaign. After all, no one was going to wade into the middle of the pond to remove it.

But then came the rain—a solid week of rain. During the first few days, the sign slipped sideways, just a little. It was crooked but still visible. As the rain continued to soak the east coast, the sign gradually tilted more and more until by the end of the week, the weight of the one side had pulled the rest of the sign into the water, entirely out of sight.

And so my sign is no more. Will I go down, too?

November 5, 1980 (Day after election)

Yes, I guess my sunken sign was an omen. I lost. And so did Jimmy Carter, and many other Democrats, some with outstanding national reputations. All of us defeated.

The hostages in Iran, the fuel shortage, the high inflation rate, and for me, the overwhelming registration deficit, the number of organizations out to replace me, and an aggressive opponent spelled defeat.

Today I have been receiving phone calls, even some personal visits. For the most part, I manage to keep upbeat, but just once, the tears flowed when a good friend stopped by. Aside from my own dislike of being personally repudiated, I feel guilty. Guilty for letting down all my volunteers and workers. The horrible day after question is, "What could I have done differently?"

Howard says a few votes here or there wouldn't have changed things. I know, but a couple hundred here or there could have. I wonder how Jimmy Carter feels. He lost it not only for himself, but also for the rest of us. If he had lived up to expectations, he would still be in office and so would I. So I can blame my defeat on him and on the fact that there are over twice as many Republicans as Democrats in my district. But not in a hundred years will I ever say that my opponent was a better person.

But back to earth. We need milk and I can't stand seeing another person. I'll call Howard at work and ask him to stop at the grocery store.

November 8, 1980

I'm finally setting foot outside of the house.

At the bank today I met an older man who has been a good supporter over the past years.

"Sorry you lost, Helen, but you know something? I've learned time and time again in life that when one door closes, another opens. You'll find these words true for you, too."

Maybe.

December 10, 1980

Tomorrow's my last day as a member of the House of Representatives. I think I'm sad, but I'm also relieved.

December 17, 1980

Home for good.

Last week we heard the usual speeches from the podium about how much legislators had enjoyed their years in the Legislature—the best years of their lives. Imagine. I didn't say anything, not that I haven't enjoyed my years in the House and felt it a great privilege, but my mind was on my own past. As I leaned back in my leather chair and studied the *Passage of the Hours* painting, I thought of my own passage of time—the long journey beginning with the Democratic caucus of ten people in 1967 ending here in the Pennsylvania House of Representatives. I'm glad I traveled this road.

The actual end was tough when Sam threw his arms around me to tell me he would miss me. A few tears slipped out—from my eyes and from his.

Chapter Twenty-six

November 10, 1981

It's been almost a year since I've written in my journal, but now that I've returned to my addiction to politics, I feel like writing about my recent experiences.

I've had a good year, delving into family genealogy, traveling to Europe with Howard, and catching up on friends and family. But even while enjoying these activities, I felt I was just biding time until the day I would find my niche in government again.

Last year in my disappointment, I really did think I was finished with politics forever, but now I'm more caught up in its intrigue than ever. I don't understand this pull on me to want to be in state government. I continue to seek opportunities to place myself back into the political scene.

I serve on several statewide women's committees urging women to run for public office; and every time I'm in Harrisburg for these meetings, I wend my way to the Capitol, just to keep my name alive and to chat with people.

One of my acquaintances who holds a position in state government has been in contact with the governor, a Republican, in hopes of finding me a position. We'll see what happens.

Meanwhile, my head still churns with my experiences during those four years in the Legislature. I saw something in the paper the other day that brought back memories of that angry photographer who didn't want me to stand with the male legislators.

This time it was a formal photo of the leaders of the world's major industrial countries during a banquet at the Imperial Palace in Tokyo. Spouses were also in the photo.

Standing with the men—Prime Minister Major, President Clinton, Chancellor Kohl, President Yeltsin and other world leaders—was Canadian Prime Minister Kim Campbell, the lone female head of state. In front of the world leaders sat their spouses, all female.

I wondered if Ms. Campbell had to argue for the right to stand with her fellow heads of state. I wondered if she had angered the photographer. I wondered if she had made everyone uncomfortable.

And then it struck me. Ms. Campbell had no spouse. Ergo, no problem.

December 9, 1981

Three weeks ago, I drove to Harrisburg at the request of the governor's aide responsible for filling vacancies in the executive branch. I was on time but he arrived two hours late and, without apologies, he began:

"We have several vacancies on boards and regional agencies that could be good for you," he said as he flipped through some lists in front of him. "Here's a vacancy on an agriculture agency right in your own county—-and here's the Labor Relations Board. You might be interested in one of these."

"It sounds like I could live at home if I went with the agriculture agency, doesn't it?" I asked. "If I went with the labor position, I guess I would have to spend more time in Harrisburg,"

"In the first place, both positions require Senate confirmation," he said. "Yes, you could live at home if you went with the agriculture agency and come to Harrisburg once or twice a month for meetings. But the labor board would require you to be here at least three days a week." He checked his watch.

"Tell you what," he said, rising from his chair. "I'm already late for another meeting. Why don't you think about it and I'll do some checking around, then we can meet again next week."

I wanted to ask more questions, but he zoomed out the door before I even stood up.

Maybe I should have sought the position in the agriculture agency since we have many farms in our area and I had served on the House Agriculture Committee. And, best of all, I could live at home. But the Labor Relations Board sounded more enticing, the pay was better, and I thought my experience on the school board would be of value. After talking it over with Howard, I decided to seek that position.

This past week, I met with Harry Watson, the governor's legislative assistant responsible for shepherding nominations through the Senate.

"You may have trouble getting enough votes for confirmation to the Labor Relations Board," he advised. "With Republicans in the minority, we don't have enough votes to approve your confirmation, so you'll need to find votes from some of your Democratic friends. Do you think your senator from home will support you?"

"I think so," I responded and within a few minutes, I was on the Senate side of the Capitol, seated in Jack McCormick's office.

"Sure. I'll support you," he said. "And I should be able to round up a few more votes, but you don't think this is just a Republican ploy to keep you from running again, do you? Think about it."

"I drove home happy, thinking I was on my way to being confirmed, but I did feel uneasy about Jack's suggestion that the Republicans were playing games with me. Since I don't plan to run again, it doesn't matter.

December 10, 1981

I was astounded to receive a phone call from Jack today, telling me he couldn't support me after all.

"It's like this, Helen—" and he went on to tell me that organized labor would not tolerate my nomination because the seat on the Labor Relations Board for which I was being nominated has always been held by a person from the ranks of labor.

"I'm sorry, Helen, but I just can't support you," he ended.

"But I'd be fair in my decisions. I know I would," I responded.

"That's not the point," he continued. "It's their seat and they want to hold onto it."

"It seems I'm destined to always want a seat that belongs to someone else," I muttered, half to myself, as I hung up the phone.

I'm not about to give up. After the holidays I'll go back to Harrisburg to try to find the necessary votes.

January 5, 1982

When I arrived in Harrisburg on Monday, I first went to see Harry. We discussed the fact that my senator would not support me.

"Look," he said. "This could be an experience in futility. Without the support of your own senator, confirmation is almost impossible. If you withdraw your name now, in a few months we'll try to come up with another position. We'd love to have you back in Harrisburg. The governor has always respected you."

I told him I would think it over, left the Capitol, and checked into a local hotel.

The next day I went about seeking affirmative votes. I first visited senators I knew to be independent. I received sympathy and I even sensed a desire to vote for me, but the Democratic caucus had voted to reject my nomination. No Democratic senators, no matter how independent, were willing to go against the wishes of their caucus on this matter.

I stopped by Harry's office again. He advised me to seek out some of the Democratic leaders in the slight chance they may reconsider their caucus position. How humiliating it was for me, a Democrat, to walk into Democratic senators' offices begging for support.

When I entered the large office of one of the Senate leaders seated behind his desk at the far end of the room, I felt him eyeing me up and down as I approached. I introduced myself even though I had made an appointment and he knew who I was. He remained seated. He said nothing nor did he ask me to sit down. After I gave my speech, he nodded and returned to some papers on his desk. I assumed he was finished with me, but as I left the room, I felt his eyes escorting my every step.

I hate this whole process. So degrading. Maybe I should withdraw my nomination, but I can't. Something in me makes me want to see this to the end.

Chapter Twenty-seven

January 26, 1982

Yesterday was my hearing before the Senate Labor Committee. It was similar to hearings for the confirmation of national officials, although with fewer people and no television.

Committee members were seated behind a long table mounted with portable podiums. I was at a small table across from them. In the audience were staff people, several members of the press, and lobbyists from labor organizations. Also present was Elaine, my faithful campaign manager, who loves going to Harrisburg.

The questioning went something like this.

"Why did you support amendments to outlaw teachers' right to strike?"

"Because I consider teaching children every bit as important as the work of police and firemen, both of whom are prohibited from striking."

"Why didn't you support additional funds for public education?"

"I did support additional funds, but not to the extent requested by the governor."

"You almost had a teachers' strike in your district

when you were president of your school board, didn't you?"

"Yes. The board was more than fair in their salary package and in matters relating to working conditions. Fortunately, both sides gave in a little and a strike was averted."

And so it went. After almost an hour, I was told the senators would go into executive session in another room. They would return to the conference room shortly to announce their decision.

Elaine and I went to the snack shop for coffee. When we returned fifteen minutes later, the senators were back in the room. Apparently, there had been little discussion. By one vote, they agreed to send my nomination to the full Senate for consideration.

Elaine and I headed home.

This morning I received a phone call from Harry, the governor's legislative assistant.

"Helen, your nomination is in trouble. How about if I ask the governor to withdraw it? It doesn't look good for your confirmation and we want to spare you any unpleasantness."

Spare me any unpleasantness? Hah! The governor and the senators were not worried about me; they were worried about themselves, particularly my local senator who couldn't follow through on his promise. Of course, they wanted me to pull out. I was an embarrassment.

"No way," I responded, keeping my thoughts to myself. "Maybe someone will have a change of heart."

"If that's what you want, okay, but I think you're making a big mistake. It could get nasty," he warned.

"I think I can take it. Thanks for your concern," I said trying to keep from slamming down the phone.

I must confess to having some uneasiness. I don't

relish another defeat, but I know the men want me to withdraw my name just so they can have an easy out.

My confirmation vote before the full Senate is scheduled for early next month.

Chapter Twenty-eight

February 10, 1982

Last Tuesday was my confirmation vote before the full Senate.

Since both Howard and Elaine were busy, I drove alone to Harrisburg. My first stop was at Harry's office. I nearly bumped into him as he charged through the door just as I was opening it. He lit a cigarette as we walked into the hallway together and stood by the marble railing overlooking the magnificent rotunda and the wide marble steps.

His words were not encouraging.

"I've just talked with the majority leader and he said two of the 'yes' votes are out of town. Even if we can find several Democrats to support your confirmation, it appears the numbers aren't there." He stopped for a moment and then continued when I failed to respond. "The governor is still willing to withdraw the nomination, Helen. It won't be a problem."

I stood with both elbows leaning on the marble railing. I had often stood like this, leaning my head over the side so as to watch people down below in the rotunda. Finally I turned to him.

"We've been through this before, Harry. I'm going for the vote. Let's see where everyone stands. Okay?"

"All right," he sighed. "It's your call. I'll see you later."

After he left, I continued to scan the rotunda. It was fun watching people move through the swinging doors. Some of them were obviously visitors who looked lost until they spotted the information desk. One legislator was taking his daily laps, a secretary at his side jotting down notes. State workers and lobbyists hurried across the Capitol floor, imbedded with Mercer tiles from Bucks County. Across the vastness of the rotunda was the Senate where, in all probability, the doors of state government would close on me, forever.

Turning from the panoramic view, I walked down the winding marble stairs to the first floor where I greeted a few friends before continuing down the hall to a Republican leader's office. He's been a friend for several years.

"Your big day, huh, Helen?" greeted his secretary.

"I guess," I responded. "Is the senator in?"

"No, he's in a leadership meeting but he did mention you would be coming. Why don't you hang up your coat," she said, "and how about a cup of coffee?"

"Sounds good. Thanks, Mary. Any idea when they'll vote on my confirmation?"

"I think both parties are going into caucus at four," she said, "which means they probably won't vote until after dinner. You know how that goes."

"Sure," I said, taking the coffee she offered. "They may not get to me until nine or so."

Just then Senator Waldo arrived.

"Hi, Helen. All set, are you?" he smiled as he came over to shake my hand.

"I'm here," I responded, "but I'm told that I shouldn't

be very optimistic."

"I guess not, but you never know what might change a vote here or there. I have the schedule for you," he continued, going through some papers on his desk. But before he could find the list, someone called from the doorway.

"Meeting in the governor's office. Right away."

"I gotta run, Helen, but the way it looks, we won't go into session until after dinner." He darted out the door.

"If that's the case, Mary, I'm going to a friend's house and will be back around eight. That should be okay, shouldn't it?" I asked.

"You could probably wait until nine and hope they'll be here by then," she replied.

After a pleasant few hours and a good Pennsylvania Dutch dinner at the home of my college roommate, I returned to the Capitol around eight. As I suspected, no senators were in sight. Finally, around nine they began to arrive, after their leisurely dinners of fine food and drink. I sat in the visitors' balcony to observe my fate.

They straggled in over the next thirty minutes, and at nine-thirty the chair gaveled the Senate to order. Some of them were noisy and one had already gone to sleep at his desk. It was not until almost eleven when the motion to confirm me was called up.

I ended up five votes shy for confirmation.

As I retrieved my coat from Senator Waldo's office, he came in.

"I'm sorry, Helen. It wasn't personal, you know," he said. "Anything I can do to help? You're not going home tonight, are you?"

"No to both. I'm going to my college roommate's house. Goodnight. Thanks for your concern."

When I told Janet and her husband the results, they

were solicitous and wondered what they could do for me.

"Nothing, thanks. I'm so exhausted I just want a hot bath and go to bed."

I slept fitfully and awoke the next morning in a rage.

"Sleep well, Helen?" Janet asked as I appeared in the dining room. She stopped short as she saw I had my coat on. "Aren't you staying for breakfast?"

"Yes, but first there's something I must do," I said, tearing out to my car.

For several years my "You've Got a Friend in Pennsylvania" bumper sticker had been a source of joy. Traveling in other states, people had gone out of their way to tell Howard and me how beautiful Pennsylvania is and how friendly the people are. I had agreed. But that morning, Pennsylvania was anything but a friendly state. I was bitterly angry. My emotions had caught up with the events of the previous night.

I grabbed a little corner of the bumper sticker and yanked as crisply as I could. It came off in one piece. I tore it in half, then in half again, and again, and again, until only little pieces remained. I stalked into the house, and thrust my once highly-regarded bumper sticker into the trashcan.

I want nothing more to do with state government or politics—ever again. The whole place is one stinking sewer.

February 19, 1982

Two days ago, a Democratic Senate leader who had voted against my confirmation phoned.

"Hi, Helen," he said. "Sorry about how things went.

We're just wondering. Would you like to have your confirmation reconsidered? We could probably vote again next—"

"Are you out of your mind?" I hollered. "Why under the sun would I want to undergo that torture again?"

"Just asking. Just –" were the last words I heard as I slammed down the phone, and in so doing, I slammed the door on Pennsylvania politics, forever.

Chapter Twenty-nine

April 5, 1982

Last week, I had lunch with Jean who served as a cabinet officer during my years in the Legislature. As we reminisced about our days in Harrisburg, she suddenly grabbed my arm.

"I'm glad I'm out of that whole political mess, aren't you?" she asked.

"Most of the time, yes. I like myself better now," I replied. "I seem to be a nicer person. Do you know what I mean?"

"Exactly! That's it," she said, her eyes bright with understanding. "I'm not fighting with someone all the time. I don't have to defend myself and the governor. I don't have to argue with legislators, and I don't have to answer reporters."

I picked up where she left off.

"No more lobbying groups to badger me. No more nasty meetings with angry constituents. No more ugly photos of myself in the newspaper. No more confirmation hearings."

"It's such a relief," she added. "I like myself better now, too."

And then she smiled and added, "But I wouldn't have missed it for the world, would you?"

Of course not.

A Note to the Reader

Even though Helen thought her days in state government were over, they were not. She was appointed to the position of legislative liaison in the Department of Education, which gave her much pleasure for an additional four years. And, yes, she had many more walks along the Susquehanna River.

6 - 2004